THE 70'S / CHALLENGE AND OPPORTUNITY

THE 70's / CHALLENGE AND OPPORTUNITY

PUBLISHED UNDER THE AUSPICES OF THE AGRICULTURAL COMMITTEE OF THE GREATER DES MOINES CHAMBER OF COMMERCE WITH THE COOPERATION OF THE IOWA STATE UNIVERSITY CENTER FOR AGRICULTURE AND ECONOMIC DEVELOPMENT ﬌

THE IOWA STATE UNIVERSITY PRESS, AMES, IOWA

THE NATIONAL FARM INSTITUTE, a forum organized to develop wider understanding of agricultural problems, particularly as they relate to business and labor, is planned and conducted by a subcommittee of the Agricultural Committee of the Greater Des Moines Chamber of Commerce. It is politically impartial, being sponsored by the following committee in cooperation with farm organizations, farm press, Iowa State University, and others.

Members of the committee for the 1970 program, "The 70's: Challenge and Opportunity," were as follows:

NATIONAL FARM INSTITUTE

© 1970 The Iowa State University Press
Ames, Iowa 50010 · All rights reserved
Printed in U.S.A.
International Standard Book Number: 0–8138–1395–6
Library of Congress Catalog Card Number: 78–137092

CONTENTS

FOREWORD

THE NATIONAL FARM INSTITUTE spans a third-century of unbelievable technological advancement in agriculture. Six-horse hitches on two-bottom gangs were still commonplace when "Farm Tenancy" was discussed at the first Institute back in 1937. By 1965 when the Des Moines forum centered its attention on world trade, diesel-powered hydrostatic tractors were pulling eight-bottom plows and modern science had more than doubled farm efficiency.

Conceived in the mid-1930's when the effects of depressions and dust bowls were still painfully evident, the National Farm Institute rapidly became a platform for progressive discussion and debate. Although originally planned to appeal primarily to farmers, its horizons soon broadened to encompass all segments of the nation's agricultural economy.

Farsighted leaders in Iowa farm circles first suggested a farm forum for Des Moines in the early thirties, when the depression was at its worst. By the summer of 1936 the idea of a National Farm Institute had crystallized. Leaders in industry, labor, and education joined with farmers and editors in promoting the project. The Greater Des Moines Chamber of Commerce, through its Agricultural Committee, assumed sponsorship of the Institute.

Among the dedicated men in the original planning sessions who later served as chairmen were W. W. Waymack, Clifford Gregory, and J. S. Russell. Others who have assumed the arduous responsibility of the chairmanship include Kirk Fox, Don E. Edison, B. W. Lodwick, Dick Hanson, Richard Albrecht, Wayne Pritchard, Wayne Swegle, and John Airy. Iowa State University staff members have helped with Institute planning each year and have been regular program participants.

As spelled out in the Foreword seen in each year's program, the Institute seeks open and objective discussion. A theme is chosen each year. Farm-related problems that cut across the whole economic pattern of the nation are tackled. Free discussion of topics pertaining to the general theme are encouraged. Audience participation is always solicited.

Every effort has been made to keep the annual sessions on a nonpartisan basis. No resolutions are adopted nor is any consensus sought. It is believed, however, that the open discussion—which on occasion has assumed the proportions of heated debate—stimulates thinking that will lead to wiser decisions.

Program planning for each Institute begins about seven months prior to the event. Many frustrations and disappointments arise. Adverse weather frequently strikes. Nevertheless, attendance at the Institute has been consistently good, and interest remains high. Each year's theme has recognized current problems confronting agriculture and the nation—and frequently the world.

In its opening program in 1937 the National Farm Institute dealt with farm tenancy, then a burning issue in America's farm economy. The following year the farmer's stake in imports and exports became the Institute theme—a topic under discussion a number of times since. In 1939 came the first major recognition of farm interdependence with other segments of our economy. The theme that year was "Agriculture, Industry, and Labor."

World War II found the National Farm Institute focusing full attention on agriculture's part in the global conflict. Topics during the war period included farm preparedness, agriculture's concern in the fight for freedom, and the happier 1944 theme—"The Farmer Looks Ahead to Peace."

World problems came closer and closer to midwestern farmers. The Institute responded with programs such as "Agriculture and World Reconstruction," "American Agriculture in World Affairs," "What Price Plenty?" and "Our Part in Building a Free World."

Throughout the fifties, the Institute became concerned with burgeoning farm production and diminishing farm returns. "Capital Needs of Agriculture," "Price Supports, Tariffs, and Foreign Trade," "A Fair Share for Farmers," "New Approaches to the Farm Problem," and "New Markets and Techniques" were among the NFI themes during this period.

Reexamination of farm resources and technology and the increasing opportunities in world trade have been under consideration since the 1958 theme, "Redirection of Agricultural Resources." In 1960 Institute visitors heard lively discussions on the topic "Farm Agencies Must Face a New Direction." "Agricultural Trade and Aid" was emphasized in 1962, with a look at our growing economy the following year. "Educational Needs of Rural People" was the topic under discussion in 1964. The relation of world trade to farm returns was explored again in 1965 when the Institute theme was "Imports, Exports, and Farm Prosperity."

Speakers have been drawn from all parts of the United States, as well as from England, Scotland, Russia, China, Sweden, India, Japan, Lebanon, Italy, Australia, Canada, and several other foreign lands.

Among those coming from across the seas were Lady Astor, Lord Marley, Sir Wilmont Lewis, and the Earl of Waldegrave, all of the United Kingdom; Douglas Harkness, Canada; Dr. Sicco Mansholt, of the European Common Market; and Dr. Allan Callaghan, Australia.

Highly placed government officials have recognized the National Farm Institute with their presence and participation. Henry A. Wallace, a native Iowan, came first as President Roosevelt's Secretary of Agriculture and later as Vice-President. A dozen or more members of presidential cabinets have attended. Among them were General George C. Marshall, Cordell Hull, Frances Perkins, Adolph Berle, John Foster Dulles, Dean Rusk, Herbert Brownell, and Fred Seaton.

Seven U.S. Secretaries of Agriculture—Wallace, Anderson, Wickard, Brannan, Benson, Freeman, and Hardin—have contributed to Institute programs through the years.

Captains of industry are regular participants, too. Fowler McCormick, Samuel White, H. J. Heinz II, Morris Sayre, and Paul Willis are a few of the agribusinessmen who have been on the program. Labor has been represented by James Corey, Sidney Hillman, Victor Reuther, and others.

Women have frequently graced the Institute stage. In addition to Secretary of Labor Frances Perkins, I would mention Mrs. Raymond Sayre, chairman of the Associated Country Women of the World, and Master Farm Homemaker Mrs. Helen Kelleher. Most major farm organization spokesmen—Ed O'Neal, Lewis Tabor, Allan Kline, Jim Patton, Herschel Newsom, Charles Shuman, Oren Lee Staley, and Tony Dechant, to name a few—have participated.

Other speakers have included a number of U.S. senators and congressmen and several governors. Leaders in the field of education and religion have contributed to the Des Moines forum, along with editors, military officials, and many others. All told, some 800 people have participated in National Farm Institute programs since Dr. Theodore Schultz, then a department head at Iowa State University, served as the opening speaker in 1937.

Great loyalty has been shown the National Farm Institute by its patrons. Some 70 persons have attended 25 or more of the 32 Institutes to date. In 1963, in connection with the twenty-fifth National Farm Institute, a Pioneers Club was formed. Certificates of appreciation were given by the Des Moines Chamber of Commerce to everyone attending all 25 Institutes. A breakfast program is now an annual event for the Farm Institute Pioneers.

Since 1937, when the Des Moines event came into being, many other cities and communities have patterned meetings along the lines of the Des Moines program. New Orleans, Denver, Minneapolis, Spokane, Mason City and Winnipeg, Canada, are among those who have undertaken meetings similar to those conducted by the "Granddaddy" of them all—the National Farm Institute.

HERB PLAMBECK
Member, National Farm Institute Founders Committee
Chairman, National Farm Institute Pioneers

THE 70'S / CHALLENGE AND OPPORTUNITY

LAUREN SOTH

Editor, Editorial Page
Des Moines Register and Tribune

1 | NATIONAL PRIORITIES IN THE 70'S

As we begin the seventies, we hear talk about our trillion-dollar economy, about America's enormous capacity to produce goods and services. (Just when we were getting used to billions—now we must learn to think in trillions.) We Americans seem to be able to make and provide anything we want.

But the more prosperity we have, the more goods and services we want. As our output goes up and up, the gap between what we have and what we want does not close. Our needs and wants always seem to keep racing ahead of our ability to fulfill them.

So we have to choose what we want most and decide how to put first things first. In the current manner of speaking, we must set priorities.

Where and how we assign priorities in a democracy is determined by our political processes—elections, lobbying, and so on—and by the decisions of business firms, labor unions, and consumers. Experts and government officials have comparatively little to do with the main decisions, but by gathering facts and providing analysis they can help us all do a better job of selecting priorities.

The purpose of the National Farm Institute is to make ourselves think, —about the hardest task which confronts the human animal. It is much easier to obey our prejudices and not let the facts confuse us.

Everybody knows that we are making all kinds of mistakes in assigning priorities in this country. The trouble is, we don't agree on what the mistakes are. There are a number of methods we can use in trying to sort out the mistakes and to set better priorities. We can resort to astrology and find our answers in the stars; we can take the advice of specialists (such as the professional military leaders or the scientists); we can place our faith in Providence; we can slavishly follow a theoretical doctrine (such as socialism or capitalism); or we can make choices on practical grounds.

Mark Twain suggested a plan for eliminating mistakes, which rather appeals to me. In one of his lectures he said:

I have this theory for doing a great deal of good. . . . Every transgression, every crime you commit—the lesson of it, I mean—make it permanent; impress it so that you may never commit that same crime again as long as you live, then you will see yourself what the logical result of that will be—that you get interested in committing crimes. You will lay up in that way, course by course, the edifice of a personally perfect moral character.
You cannot afford to waste any crime, they are not given to you to be thrown away, but for a great purpose. There are 462 crimes possible and you cannot add anything to this, you cannot originate anything. These have been all thought out, all experimented on and have been thought out by the most capable men in the penitentiary. . . .
When you have committed your 462, you . . . have ascended the staircase of faultless creation . . . complete with absolute moral perfection, and I am more than two-thirds up there. It is immense inspiration to find yourself climbing that way and have not much further to go.

Following the Mark Twain line, perhaps we could argue—in this time of much dissent and questioning of priorities—that the United States has made enough mistakes and committed enough crimes to be well along the way to moral virtue and right priorities. It certainly is true that a great many Americans want to change our present set of priorities. And, as a nation, we are making changes in the way we use our resources—changes in the things we are putting first.

Before going into the revision of priorities, however, our capacity to produce—what we have to work with—should be discussed. The United States now has a trillion-dollar economy—a reference to the gross national product, or the sum of the values of all the goods and services produced in one year. For America's GNP for 1970 will come very close to one trillion dollars. The estimate of the President's economic advisers is $985 billion.

In 1929 the GNP was about $100 billion, illustrating the immensity of this productive effort. When we adjust this figure for the changes in prices and the makeup of the output of the last 40 years, the GNP of 1929 is valued at about $250 billion in today's terms.

Thus the country has increased its output of goods and services in real value by four times in the last 40 years. The population has also increased considerably in the last 40 years. In 1930 the census showed 123 million Americans (not including Alaskans and Hawaiians.) In 1970 we have about 210 million people. In the last 40 years, while the population has been less than doubling (increasing by about two-thirds), our output has increased four times. The real value of the goods and services per person has gone up about two and one-half times in that period. In round numbers, we could say that the GNP per person this year is $5,000. In dollars of the same purchasing power, the output in 1929 was about $2,000 per person.

This is not income per person, and still less, it is not spendable income per person. It is the value of the nation's production, that is, what we have available as a nation to allocate to different purposes. Some of it must be allocated to replacement of worn-out equipment or depreciation. The rest of it can be used for new private investment, for military expenditures, and for various other forms of collective consumption such as education, which is partly investment. The rest goes for personal consumption.

Choosing between what we spend and invest publicly or collectively and what we spend and invest privately is part of the problem of priority setting. Each year, at the current rate of economic growth, we are adding around $50 billion to the GNP. Unfortunately, in the late sixties much of this annual increment in dollars has been inflation —marking up the price tags and the wage rates—and not real growth, and that will be the case in 1970.

A major priority decision must be made as we start this decade. Walter Heller, the former chairman of the President's Council of Economic Advisers, stated it, "the problem is to BRAKE inflation and BREAK the inflation mentality in the 70's without generating intolerable unemployment and social tensions."

To a large extent this problem of economic policy is a question of economic priorities. We must choose between degrees of unemployment and inflation or degrees of wage and price fixing by the government—all unpalatable.

Do we want to reduce the inflation rate from 5 or 6 percent a year in retail prices to, say, 2 percent a year, at the cost of a rise in unemployment from 3 percent to 6 percent of the working population? This 6 percent unemployment rate would mean at least 12 percent unemployment among the most vulnerable members of the work force —the least educated, the black, the poor, and the eighteen- and nineteen-year-olds.

There is no painless solution. If we want to continue vigorous economic growth to keep unemployment at a low level and to provide expanding resources to use for the national welfare, we may have to put up with a considerable amount of inflation or subject ourselves to wage and price controls that are inefficient, arbitrary, and generally a nuisance.

Or to put it another way, if we want to stop inflation in its tracks, we may have to pay the price of more social unrest—particularly in the cities but also in rural areas—a decline in farm income, and a loss of national output.

In economics we are still primitives. We do not really know how to prevent inflation without strangling production.

Of the other main priority questions that must be settled, the most important is the allocation of national manpower, industrial capacity, and other resources to military purposes. You will notice that I did not say "national defense" because there is a difference of opinion about the relation of the military establishment to national defense.

Of course everyone wants the nation securely defended; the question is: How large a military establishment contributes to that purpose? When does the military side of our foreign policy become so preeminent that it is a factor of insecurity, a cause of war, or a weakening of true national defense?

Many of us think that the United States, in spite of its long traditions of antimilitarism, has come dangerously close to building such an enormous military machine as to weaken the national defense. We are now allocating close to $75 billion a year for military purposes. This is a $5 billion reduction from the high level of a year ago. But the armed forces are not exactly starving for funds. The $75 billion is about 40 percent of the federal government expenditure and about 8 percent of the GNP. This is not only the largest outlay for military purposes of any country in the world (including the Soviet Union with a liberal allowance in the budget for hidden military expenditures), it is also the highest in percentage of national product except for Russia.

Such a mammoth military machine tends to make work for itself. It tends to cause the nation's civilian leaders to see military solutions to international problems.

The military system provides services for the nation that are indispensable; but it is up to the people of the United States, through their elected civilian leaders, to decide how much of such services are required. We have been drifting into the habit of allowing the military men and the industries associated with the military establishment to make these decisions.

We have been so afraid the Russians might get ahead of us in missiles or total killing power and they have been so afraid of us that both sides have been piling up ridiculous capacity for overkill. If we can wipe out half the cities of the Soviet Union in one blow, what good does it do to add more nuclear weapons? Obviously, both countries would be just as safe (if you can call it that) with half their present destructive force if both would cut back. Maybe we should put higher priority on trying to reduce weaponry than in trying to get ahead.

Congress has been taking a keener look at military spending, and the current trend in military outlays is downward. If the Nixon Administration continues on its present path, we may slice out $10 billion from the military budget during 1971-72. That would be enough to more than double the federal antipoverty program.

Aside from the fundamental questions of how much and what kinds of weapons and military units, there is the question of waste in military operations and preparations for war. This is simply colossal. It rises out of fear and the turning over of decisions to the military experts without checking up on them. We are spending much more of our productive resources for that purpose than needed, even if we should assume the present size of the armed forces is advisable.

In the last 15 years about $9 billion were invested in 67 major military contracts which were subsequently canceled, either because the weapons did not meet specifications or the military decided it had no use for them. The Budget Bureau reported that in 13 missile and aircraft programs since 1955, at a cost of $40 billion, more than 60 percent of the electronic components failed to perform acceptably. That is just a small sample.

It is really strange that many people who think $3 billion a year for federal farm programs to help farmers earn decent incomes is outrageous will blandly overlook enormously wasteful spending for military goods and guaranteed profits for firms that supply these goods.

Setting new priorities to fight poverty, clear up slums in cities and in rural areas, fight crime, and provide better job training and education—and getting the money for this from the military budget—might well give us a stronger military defense. It could do so by cutting out fat, reducing duplication, and placing emphasis on arms limitation negotiations. It certainly would result in more progress on curing our domestic ills and more security at home. Many of us think security in the streets of Chicago is more important than security in the streets of Saigon.

We could argue endlessly about priorities within the fields of education, welfare, and other social improvements—priorities between public spending for these purposes and private spending.

However, these are small questions indeed compared with the big one of military versus other activities. If we placed military outlays under control, it would be easier to deal with the others. One reason for this is that every dollar saved in outlays for military purposes is a bigger contribution toward fighting inflation than a dollar saved in the farm program, for example, or in the food programs for poor people.

Military spending goes for goods that return nothing to the civilian economy. If military spending could be reduced by $10 billion or, with an end of the war in Vietnam, perhaps $25 billion, that would knock the stuffing out of inflation faster than anything else we can do.

Other authors in this book will discuss priorities in public and private action in agriculture. This chapter will provide a background for looking at these problems. Intelligent ordering of priorities requires a hard look at military as well as other uses of our resources. We cannot afford, rich as we are, to accept military budget proposals without regard to nonmilitary goals.

THOMAS R. FORD

Rural Sociologist
University of Kentucky

2 | PRIORITIES OF RURAL WELFARE

We live today in troubled times. No doubt each age considers its tribulations to be greater than those of earlier generations, just as each age feels that the pace of social change is faster in its own time than in previous eras. There is certainly much evidence to support the view that the world in which we live today is in fact changing at an ever quickening pace. There is equally good evidence establishing a relationship between rapid social change and the prevalence of both individual and social disorganization. Yet I am not persuaded that change in itself is the source of the deep unrest that pervades the spirit of this nation. For we are a nation conceived in change and in a very real sense dedicated to the proposition that change is a necessary condition for the realization of the goals and values which we cherish. The real issue of national concern is whether the changes that are taking place, both planned or unplanned, are leading us where we wish to go. There is considerable sentiment, especially among the young but certainly not limited to them, that as a body politic we are not merely disoriented but so mired in the daily routines of getting and spending that we have either forgotten what we wished to achieve as a nation or simply no longer care.

Recognizing the limitation of all analogies, there are certain similarities between nations and men that have moved from youth to middle age. In our youth we are possessed of noble ideals and lofty aspirations. If we are of a pragmatic turn of mind, as most Americans tend to be, we also recognize that the attainment of our aspirations requires some economic security, and we set to the task of achieving it, confident that once it is accomplished we can turn again to those youthful ambitions. But as the responsibilities and requirements of adult status fall more heavily upon us and the elusive goal of security moves always just ahead of us like the pot of gold at the end of the rainbow, we postpone again and again the realization of those dreams of our youth. We adjust our reach to fit our grasp and are sometimes comforted by the recognition that in some ways we have exceeded our own expectations: we are making more money, have greater job responsibilities, live in a bigger house, or are able to send our children to better schools. But such complacencies can be shattered by the sudden awareness that our children, grown to youth themselves and possessed of their own ideals and aspirations, do not see us in such a kindly light. To them we often appear materialistic, self-seeking, and enslaved in the mechanical requirements of a system that at best ignores and at worst exploits those of our fellowmen who stand in greatest need. Should we protest that we once had dreams of our own like theirs, it only makes matters worse—adding spiritual prostitution to those sins with which we are already charged.

So, too, we find ourselves as a middle-aged nation, with our two-hundredth birthday looming just ahead. We have not yet secured those rights of life, liberty, and the pursuit of happiness for all our citizens. But we have made progress, and some day soon we will get around to finishing up the incompleted tasks of democracy. First, we need to achieve national economic security. We have not done badly though; our gross national product is the highest in the world, and we have more television sets, bathtubs, automobiles, and telephones than all other nations combined. We have worked hard to achieve these things, and we feel deserving of some commendation for our efforts.

We need not look to our youth for such commendation. They point out rightly that the goals for which this nation was founded did not include two cars in every garage and a twenty-one inch color television set in every living room. To them this nation has lost the vision of our founding fathers—to create a society in which all men were provided with opportunities to fulfill their legitimate ambitions and had a voice in controlling their own destinies. Our economic affluence, they charge, has not brought us closer to the realization of these dreams, it has brought only a sense of social complacency. They are not impressed by a GNP approaching $1,000 billion but rather are offended and angry that social ills and injustices still persist in this wealthy land.

Such charges make many of us uncomfortable, and we tend to retaliate in either angry or self-righteous tones, especially if the charges are accompanied by militant threats to tear down the national, social, and economic structures and replace them with some unspecified improvement. However, we do ourselves greater injustice by indignantly refusing to consider the faults charged to our society by our young people than by conceding the possibility that they contain at least the seeds of truth.

It is from this background that I wish to talk about priorities in rural welfare. It is a complex topic and one that cannot be covered adequately here. Many of the complexities have been discussed in the report <u>The People Left Behind</u> submitted by President Johnson's Commission on Rural Poverty on which I had the honor to serve. While commending this report to those who have not read it, I shall avoid the temptation to discuss its contents. Let me say only that it documents the fact largely ignored by the nation, that welfare problems of our rural society are proportionately much greater than those of our metropolitan central cities which loudly clamor for—and receive—more federal assistance. Poverty statistics recently released by the Bureau of the Census continue to show that the highest concentration of poverty relative to population is to be found outside our metropolitan areas. In fact, the proportion of the nonmetropolitan population below the federally defined poverty level—18 percent—is nearly twice the proportion for metropolitan residents—10 percent—and more than a third greater than the proportion living in metropolitan central cities—13.9 percent.

More than one out of every five farm dwellers—about 23 percent—fell below the poverty line in 1968; this was nearly double the percentage for the nonfarm population. While not unsympathetic to the economic plight of the Negro population in our metropolitan ghettos (about a fourth are classified as being in poverty), I would call to your attention that nearly two out of three Negro farm families live in poverty. It is important not to minimize their plight but to introduce some perspective—the average money income of Negro families living in central cities with a population of one million or more was higher than the average money income of white as well as Negro farm families.

It would now seem appropriate to look at welfare from a somewhat different perspective. If there is any issue on which we seem to have achieved bipartisan consensus, it is that welfare as known and practiced in this country has been a monumental failure. Having arrived at this conclusion, however, there is very little agreement about what should be done to replace it. After reviewing a number of the proposals that have been offered, few of them seem really radical enough —not in the political sense of radicalism but in the original sense of getting to the roots of the matter. The fundamental fault in our welfare systems lies in our conception of welfare, and until we alter that conceptual foundation, any other system erected upon it will develop most of the same faults as previous systems.

There are three basic misconceptions about welfare. The first—and to my mind the most damaging in its implications—is that welfare is the elimination of some social ill rather than the attainment of some desirable state. Ida Merriam of the Social Security Administration indicates that a positive definition of welfare can be easily adapted from the World Health Organization's definition of positive health: "Welfare is a state of complete physical, mental, and social well-being—not merely the absence of poverty and social disorganization."

At first blush this may sound like the semantic nitpicking of a college professor who has nothing better to do than argue about definitions. But as linguists constantly remind us, our definitions of things invariably affect the ways in which we deal with them. If we define a dentist as a man we see when we have a toothache, the chances are we will have a lot of toothaches. If we define him as a man who is supposed to keep our teeth in good shape, the probability is high that he will never have to treat us for a toothache. By the same token, by defining welfare institutions as those designed to cope with social problems, we are going to be overwhelmed with problems. Our emphasis should be a positive one that prevents problems rather than one that constantly seeks to correct those that have arisen.

A second major defect of our present concept of welfare is the view that welfare issues are primarily if not exclusively the problems of inadequate income. For all our fondness for quoting the biblical admonition that "man does not live by bread alone," we still continue to act as though we believe he does, or at least that if he has enough bread, he can buy whatever else he needs. It is this line of reasoning that sends us searching for some magic gimmick such as a negative income tax or a family support plan that will solve all our welfare problems. I have no objections to income support. I will readily concede that if man does not live by bread alone, he does live by bread at least; but we are only deluding ourselves if we think that income supplements will do the full job.

One reason they will not do the full job stems directly from a third misconception about welfare that is concerned essentially with assisting unfortunate individuals or families. Like the economic view of welfare, the fallacy of this notion lies not in its falsity, but in its being only a partial truth too often accepted as the full truth. Of course there are unfortunate individuals and families whose conditions are tragic and must be relieved. But their circumstances are more often than not a direct outgrowth of the failing social and economic institutions of poor communities, and community welfare should be just as much a matter of concern as individual welfare.

When we combine these three misconceptions of welfare, the reasons why programs based upon them are likely to fail become evident. Such programs are constantly engaged in trying to remedy the problems of individuals and families by doling out money, while the conditions which perpetuate the problems continue largely unabated.

Our highest priority for rural welfare—or all welfare for that matter—is to reorient our entire approach. We must begin to think of welfare in positive terms which encompass not only income but the entire spectrum of conditions that make life worthwhile. We must recognize that the welfare of the individual or family cannot be divorced from the welfare of the community in which he lives.

In making such a proposal, I do not have in mind the establishment of any super bureaucracies. I think we have learned by now that federal bureaucracies have limitations as well as uses, and one of their greatest limitations is dealing knowledgeably and effectively with the affairs of local communities. The fate of any community program rests fundamentally upon the citizens of that community, and it is they who must assume the ultimate responsibility for its success or failure.

Our rural communities have been derelict in accepting these responsibilities. There have been many extenuating circumstances, including inadequate economic resources and difficulties in meeting institutional needs of a dispersed population. But the deficiencies of so many of our rural institutions also stem in large part from the persistence of an agrarian philosophy that stressed independence and self-reliance of the family almost to the exclusion of other strong social institutions. While there is undoubtedly virtue in the deeply ingrained rural belief that public institutions should perform only those functions that individuals and families cannot perform for themselves, our rural people have been slow to grasp the functional limitations of the family in a complex industrial and commercial society. Just as the economic welfare of farmers requires them to organize in cooperative endeavors in the agribusiness complex, social welfare of rural citizens requires development of strong social institutions.

We should have recognized by now that failure to develop effective social institutions has been a major factor in the downward spiral of so many rural communities. Their absence has been a strong deterrent to establishing new business and industry as well as attracting professionals whose skills are sorely needed in most rural areas. Community poverty reflected in poor schools, churches, health services, and local government inevitably contributes to personal poverty by failing to develop capabilities required of individuals to lead productive lives in our modern society. Current attempts to arrest the flow of rural migrants to cities will be of little avail until we make of our rural communities areas where people want to live. Provision of minimal incomes is not enough.

In some respects it may be easier to develop first-rate communities in our rural areas than in our metropolitan areas—for the same reason it proved easier to build new cities in the bombed-out areas of Europe than in those areas that suffered little damage. We must still clean out some of the remaining social debris. The difficulties of making major social changes can scarcely be greater than those encountered in our largely ineffectual efforts to make minor repairs. The challenge of creating the new is far more compatible with our national spirit than repairing the old. Certainly any owner of a house, automobile, or electrical appliance knows that **Americans** are better builders than repairers—or at least they seem to be able to build faster and with greater enthusiasm.

In suggesting the creation of new rural communities and community institutions as a positive approach to social welfare, I am mindful of the need for an adequate economic resource base. However, I do not find the two incompatible. Much of the recent economic thought given to the idea of urban growth centers serving as the focal point for rural development areas is equally transferrable to the concept of institutional service areas. In fact, many states are already making considerable progress in this direction. Furthermore, we should be aware that the provision of services is also an economic function—our most rapidly expanding production area—which offers employment opportunities for a wide range of skills. It is also an area in which we face our greatest manpower needs—needs which have been largely unmet because our educational institutions have not done an adequate job. As we develop new communities geared to the social require-ments of our citizens, we will also be creating new and expanding job opportunities; but we must keep our priorities clear. The purpose of our communities is not to make money, but to provide every citizen an opportunity to live a rewarding life, to adequately meet his basic social needs, and to develop a respect for himself that can only be achieved through developing a respect for others.

The creation of good communities to serve rural America is an awesome task. But so was the creation of a new nation which was built on the dreams of men who sought a better way of life. In re-flecting on the conditions that led to the founding of this nation, Tocqueville wrote:

There sometimes comes a time in the history of nations when old customs are changed, old habits destroyed, old convictions shaken; when the prestige of the past disappears and when, nevertheless, instruction is still incomplete and political rights ill secured or restricted. Mankind then see their country through a dim and uncertain medium: they no longer place it in the mere soil, which to them has become inanimate earth; nor in the usages of their ances-tors, which they have been taught to consider as a yoke; nor in their religion, of which they have begun to doubt; nor in their laws, which are not of their own making; nor in the legislator, whom they dread and despise. They see it therefore nowhere . . . and they retire within a narrow and unenlightened self-interest.

What then is to be done? To go back? But a people can no more return to the feelings of their youth than a man to the infantine pleasures of his infan-tine years; they may regret, but they cannot revive them. There is nothing for us but to go forward, and to hasten to identify in the minds of the peoples individual interest with public interest.

It would appear to me that our nation has reached such a turning point as that of which Tocqueville spoke. We cannot go back; we must go forward. We must identify the individual interest with the public interest which Tocqueville saw as the key to the success of the American democracy. It is not the same as identifying the public interest with the individual interest. I do not share the despair of many of our young people that we have lost the way, that we have traded our national birthright for a mess of material pottage. But I do share the concern that every thoughtful citizen must feel about the future welfare of rural America. I also share the sentiments ex-pressed by President Nixon in his recent State of the Union address when he said, "Today, when we are the richest and strongest nation in the world, let it not be recorded that we lack the moral and spiritual idealism which made us the hope of the world at the time of our birth . . . . And above all, let us inspire young Americans with a sense of excitement, a sense of destiny, a sense of involvement in meeting the challenges we face in this great period of our history. Only then are they going to have any sense of satisfaction in their lives."

The challenge of building a new and better rural America, dedicated to meeting broadly conceived welfare goals, holds the promise of providing such an inspiration. The leadership must come not from Washington, not from the state capitals, but from communities themselves. It is there that self-interest must be identified with public interest. And it is there that responsibility for success or failure of our rural welfare must surely and inevitably lie.

JOHN A. SCHNITTKER

Economist
Kansas State University

3 | PRIORITIES IN COMMERCIAL AGRICULTURAL POLICY

We are in an era of unprecedented competition for public funds. The size of the federal budget in any year is virtually fixed by antiinflation strategies. More than ever before public money spent for one program denies funds to others.

In such a time the highest priority in commercial agricultural policy is to bring farm program spending under the most careful scrutiny and under effective control by Congress and the executive branch.

Other high priority questions include efforts to reduce the degree of imbalance between our potential annual production and the demand for farm products, revised payment formulas to increase the degree of equity among programs for major commodities, a ceiling on total payments to any producer, and a general review of price support programs for all other commodities.

It has been said that agricultural policy in the United States is at the crossroads. The year 1970 may well be such a crossroads for policy with respect to commercial agriculture.

Policies set in motion in the sixties helped clear out most of our stored commodity surpluses. We replaced some of our old objectives and programs with new machinery for supporting farm prices and incomes and for limiting farm output. We did not come to grips with the tendency toward a large and chronic excess agricultural capacity. Yet even our existing programs, administered toward that objective, have the capacity to reduce the aggregate extent of excess capacity, even though that tendency is rooted in the economic structure of agriculture.

WHAT SHOULD WE DO?

Constructive farm policy changes made in the sixties should be consolidated in the seventies. Errors made in the sixties should be corrected. By 1975 we can make substantial progress in reconciling our agricultural policy with domestic priorities and broad international trade considerations.

There is no question about the will of the people of the United States in this regard. They want to spend more on a long list of people-oriented programs such as education, health, area development, and food distribution. There are signs that Congress wants to move in that direction, but even in this rich country we cannot buy all we need or want. Each time a national political figure lists an agenda for the nation, he warns us in the same breath that we lack the money to follow it. We are often reminded that terminating the war in Vietnam will provide greater funds for domestic programs only if we can prevent the "Vietnam dividend" from being absorbed by the Pentagon.

If we are to spend more on certain activities and programs in the seventies, we will have to spend less on a great many others. That is what priority analysis is all about. As I read the public mind, prime targets for reduced spending are Vietnam, defense, foreign aid, price and income support programs for agriculture, and some other domestic programs.

What we lack in 1970 is a clear and visible crisis—a force greater than the continuing competition for public funds—to move Congress toward serious and responsible consideration of the place of agricultural policies and agricultural expenditures in the national system of priorities. Whether or not the leadership will be found—either in the administration or in Congress—to build on the legislative foundation laid in the sixties will be answered only by Congress. It was discouraging to hear and read as early as January, 1970, that it might be necessary to extend existing programs for a year or two for lack of time to consider amendments or alternatives.

THE WORLD CONTEXT

The United States does not face agricultural policy changes alone this year. Canada has serious problems arising out of glutted world grain markets. In Europe, surpluses and high budgetary costs are requiring national governments, farm organizations, and officials of the European Community to consider major reforms of the common agricultural policy. For every expert or minister who says fundamental changes cannot be considered, there is someone equally eminent to say that such changes must not be postponed.

The difficulties the European Community faces in 1970 are similar to those faced by the United States in 1960. Surpluses which appear one day as wheat, and another as barley, butter, or poultry, and budgetary costs which may go out of control, are the hallmarks of the present common agricultural policy.

In Europe, however, the situation is harder to change. The agricultural population is far greater; the difficulties of small low-income farmers are greater than a decade ago in the United States. The complex decision-making apparatus of the European Community requires that the ministers of all the countries approve major changes before they can be made effective. Beyond that there is a built-in tendency in the European Community to maintain high price guarantees despite the danger of surpluses because high prices generate high income from the variable levy system. This income is to be spent entirely on agricultural programs, including farm modernization.

THE HISTORICAL CONTEXT

Difficulties in the United States are still rooted partly in postwar policies as well as in the technological revolution. In the United States after 1947 political decisions prevented internal agricultural price guarantees from falling along with world prices, as war-induced demands declined. Parity was still king, and Congress was determined to have one last fling at ignoring reality in agricultural stabilization programs. As a result wartime price support levels were maintained for too long or were reduced too slowly. Ineffective acreage controls and rapidly increasing yields catapulted surpluses of grain, cotton, and dairy products into a surplus crisis by 1960.

This crisis would have come sooner except for a temporary escape valve provided in 1954. This was the Agricultural Trade Development and Assistance Act, commonly known as Food for Peace. It was intended to dispose of agricultural surpluses and to provide additional foreign assistance to developing countries.

By 1960 that escape valve had begun to close. Sustained objections by other exporting countries had prevented U. S. exports under that program from reaching levels which might otherwise have been achieved. Grain and milk surpluses continued to accumulate despite the greatest efforts under the Food for Peace program. Also by 1960 there was a growing realization among academic observers, if not among program operators, that in giving food to needy agricultural nations, one could do much for the long-term good of the recipient nation.

A new administration in 1961 made a number of tentative starts in an effort to find a way out of the maze of agricultural surpluses and spiraling costs. Authority to establish production control programs and to set price support levels without direct approval by Congress was denied after an acrimonious debate. Temporary production control programs for grains were enacted to forestall surplus increases. In 1962 an effort was made to enact a direct-payments program coupled with mandatory production control for wheat (which had long had such controls) and feed grains (where mandatory controls had never been accepted). This effort in Congress succeeded only for wheat, and wheat farmers soundly rejected it in a referendum in 1963.

Thus after an extended debate we turned to voluntary acreage control programs in which the incentive for participation was provided by direct government payments to producers. By the end of 1965 revised machinery for production adjustment, price support, and direct payments to farmers had been approved by Congress for feed grains, wheat, and cotton, which are produced on two-thirds of the cultivated acreage in the United States.

Under the revised programs, price supports for wheat, feed grains, and cotton were still nominally based on parity. In fact they were geared to world market prices and to the level of competing products both at home and abroad. For wheat the drop in the level of market price supports was sharp—from nearly $2.00 to $1.25 per bushel. For cotton the drop in price was from 30 to 21 cents per pound. For feed grains the drop was modest.

The key to reducing market price support levels so sharply was a program of payments which fully, and in some cases more than, compensated farmers for the decline in their market price guarantees. Payments were the "carrot" and acreage controls were the "stick" of the new policy. To qualify for payments, farmers were required to reduce their acreages. By 1967 a combination of lower price supports, direct payments, payment-related acreage controls, and increased exports had disposed of the principal surpluses. An element of luck in this record should not be overlooked. Grain exports to Europe were higher in this period than in earlier years, and in 1966 a severe drought in Asia quickly wiped out the last of the grain surpluses.

It was not possible to materially reduce the extent to which U.S. agriculture was protected from world market price levels at the same time the price and income support system was changed so radically in the sixties. Progress in relating feed grains and wheat more closely to world markets was offset by increased levels of protection for cotton and milk.

Before 1961, U.S. wheat prices were supported at approximately 60-70 cents per bushel above world levels. With the new payment system and more effective acreage controls after 1962, the average level of return (price support plus payments) for U.S. wheat is somewhat lower than before 1961, but still well above world levels.

Prior to 1961 the level of protection (above world market prices) for feed grains in the United States was very low, although export subsidies were sometimes used to make our prices competitive. After effective acreage diversion programs and direct payments were begun, feed grain export subsidies were eliminated. The level of protection for feed grains is now at or near zero. In fact the price support level for feed grains in the United States virtually establishes market prices for coarse grains in world markets.

Cotton is among the most highly protected of the major field crops produced in the United States. Before 1961 the average subsidy ranged between 30 and 40 percent of world prices. The new cotton program enacted in 1965 continued a level of protection through payments which is even higher than before. At the same time, however, it initiated a program which had the capacity to limit production and dispose of surpluses.

These differences in the degree of protection among commodities are important to future policies and programs. They are well illustrated in data made available in 1969 by the USDA, separating the functions which direct payments served in 1968 into "supply management" and "income supplement" functions (Table 3.1).

Table 3.1. Functions served by 1968 direct payments

	Supply Management		Income Supplement	
Program	Million dollars	Percent	Million dollars	Percent
Cotton	276	35	508	65
Feed grains	1,221	89	148	11
Wheat	384	51	362	49
Three programs	1,881	65	1,018	35

Note that feed grain payments in 1968 were almost entirely devoted to limiting output (supply management), while only 1/3 of total cotton payments served that function. In 1970 nearly the entire amount of $900 million for cotton payments was an income supplement. The cotton acreage allotment was increased, so it cannot be argued that a major part of cotton payments were for supply management. One-half of all wheat payments in 1968 were income supplements, but the 1970 figure was lower, since the national acreage allotment was reduced.

Cotton and wheat producers have problems in addition to a vulnerable payments position. The gross world fiber markets have gone to man-made fibers in the past twenty-five years. United States cotton has lost its place in world markets. World wheat markets are glutted, and will recover slowly. These facts deserve sympathetic attention too.

While the policy measures noted above were being taken, a major restructuring of our agriculture was continuing. This was done under pressure of low returns on many small farms, and advancing technology, and particularly under the attraction of a full-employment economy which gave many farmers a new set of options.

Now we have only 3 million farms, down from 4.2 million in 1960. The one-third of this group markets nearly 90 percent of our agricultural products; 6 percent of them account for 50 percent of all farm marketing. The 2 million farmers market just 10 percent of the total. This is important to future farm policy. A 1967 USDA report titled "Parity Returns Position of Farmers" showed that one-third of our farmers were earning on the average an income comparable to incomes earned in similar occupations. These farmers are earning parity incomes.

These structural changes will continue and may accelerate. Sometime in the seventies 6 percent of our farmers will probably be producing two-thirds of our marketings, compared with one-half today.

We are now in mid-passage, poised between the danger of drifting back into old ways and the prospect of consolidating recent gains by directing farm policy toward the future, not the past. We have the opportunity to build on the elements of the payments-price support-production adjustment system established in the mid-sixties, or to default to old programs and slogans more obsolete today than when they were first set aside by temporary statutes in the early sixties.

We could come out with an agricultural policy less vulnerable to attack both by urban critics because it costs too much and by international critics because of excessive levels of protection and resulting surplus tendencies. But we could also do worse.

THE PRIORITIES

The first priority for policy for commercial agriculture in the seventies is to bring farm program operations and spending under effective control.

In 1970 Congress did not exercise such control through the appropriations process. The executive branch was prevented from doing so by rigid payment formulas, especially in the cotton and wheat programs, and by other program provisions. Most commodity programs are financed by CCC, which borrows from the Treasury Department —back-door financing. This practice is rooted in the open-end character of our price support commitments to farmers. Under our laws we promise farmers to support prices of all they can produce (sometimes on a specified acreage) at a level fixed in advance. The cost is evaluated at the end of the period, and it usually exceeds the estimated cost.

The cost should be decided in advance, otherwise the nation risks spending money on cotton, corn, or wheat that it intended to spend on other programs. The old procedure is certainly necessary if we are to continue to make open-end commitments under our farm programs. This may have had merit as an antidepression device in the thirties, but has little merit in a time of unprecedented competition for public funds and with a federal budget that in any year is virtually fixed by the need for general price stability.

Our procedures for financing commodity programs have the effect of treating some of our lowest priority expenditure, such as huge payments to a few cotton or wheat farmers, as if they were among our highest priority expenditures. Program commitments are usually made a year in advance of the harvest; the money must then be paid out even though it has never been appropriated. Funds for food stamps, medical research, Head Start, and low-income rural housing programs are appropriated.

A second priority, essential for farmers and administrative leaders, is a willingness to compromise. The farm policy fiasco in 1959 resulted from the rigidity of both Congress and the executive branch.

A third priority is to take measures to reduce the imbalance between farm production and the market. If yields continue to rise faster than markets expand, we will soon have to divert 40-50 million acres from feed grains, instead of 30-36 million. Whatever the method—diversion or set aside—this will increase government costs. It is doubtful that the public wants the cost to increase; the only alternative is to reduce price support levels for grain in the seventies.

A fourth priority is to bring the formulas under which direct payments are computed for cotton, wheat, sugar, and wool into line with the payment formula for feed grains. Escalator provisions which virtually ensure that many of these programs will cost more each year also ought to be amended.

Feed grain payments principally serve the function of supply management. This helps to ensure relatively stable prices. There is only a negligible element of income subsidy in feed grain payments. Cotton payments are almost entirely income subsidies, and wheat payments are partly so.

Some argue that feed grain payments should be increased sharply to give farmers in the Corn Belt the same break as cotton farmers. If I judge public opinion correctly, the people of the United States would probably say the cotton and wheat payment formulas should be amended to match feed grains.

A fifth priority is to place an effective, money-saving ceiling on payments to very large farms.

The $20,000 per farm limit twice approved by the House is too high but could save some $200 million per year for higher priority public programs. A ceiling of $10,000 per commodity on any farm would save slightly more money and would be easier to administer. A ceiling of $5,000 per program would reduce payments to big farmers by $500 million per year, but some of the savings would be offset by other costs.

The claim that a $20,000 ceiling "would destroy the programs" by building new surpluses is now hopelessly transparent. Only 2 percent of all feed grain, 3 percent of all wheat, but 28 percent of all cotton is grown on farms that would be affected. Feed grains and wheat programs would scarcely be touched by a $20,000 limit. Since cotton payments actually serve the function of increasing cotton production rather than limiting it, a payment ceiling would destroy the cotton program by producing a surplus.

Large payments go to farmers who have access to the cheapest credit, the best technology, and the best markets. Large payments provide large net income streams which have become capitalized into the price of land and water. This makes it more difficult for smaller farmers to stay in business or to expand. Giant payments discredit the farm programs in the public mind. They ought to be stopped, if only to help the farmer's public image.

There are other less visible but equally vulnerable aspects of farm commodity programs which demand an early review by Congress:

1. The tobacco program should be reexamined, in light of the changing attitude toward smoking, to revise the escalator which continues to push our tobacco prices far above world prices and then requires export subsidies to compete abroad and to make it self-financing. The welfare of thousands of small tobacco farmers should be a major consideration in such a review.

2. Programs for peanuts and rice badly need amendment, especially to limit or to reduce their insulation from world markets.

3. The sugar program, up for renewal in 1971, must not permit U.S. growers to encroach further on imports from friendly and needy nations in Latin America and Asia.

4. Our entire milk economy deserves the closest scrutiny by Congress and by consumer advocates. Demands for higher prices must be assessed against the real need for greater milk production when substitutes are plentiful and cheap and world markets are glutted. The proceeds from recent milk price increases have vastly increased the asset value of dairy farms. Now that the latest price increases have been fully capitalized into fixed-asset values, we hear demands for new increases. We need to ask where it will stop and to look objectively at the alternatives.

NICK KOTZ
Political Columnist
Washington Post and Times Herald

4 | CHANGING POLITICS OF FARM PROGRAMS

The farm programs of the sixties passed Congress only because of an uneasy, tenuous alliance between liberal urban Democrats and conservative Democrats from the cotton South.

For every farm bill that was passed, there was a "deal" in which the southerners agreed to support food aid for the poor or, for the less obstructionist, some other social welfare measure.

The food stamp law went on the books in 1964 only because President Johnson used its lure to attract sufficient urban votes to pass the Wheat-Cotton Act of that year. The food stamp program was saved from strangulation in 1967 only after Congresswoman Lenore Sullivan (Dem. Mo.) staged a "peanut revolt" which convinced the southerners that a few food stamps for the black poor were well worth the lucrative peanut support program.

In 1969 the ultimate in vote trading was symbolized by Representative Mendel Rivers marching through a teller line to vote in favor of food stamps while holding his nose. The rude gesture clearly showed the South Carolinian's distaste at this political necessity. At stake was a one-year extension of the farm law, and cotton lobbyists had persuaded Rivers and other southerners that the food stamp vote was essential to save the farm bill.

Although this process of vote trading produced narrow victories for Democratic farm bills throughout the sixties the character of the interparty trading has gradually changed as urban Democrats grow increasingly restive about supporting farm subsidies and increasingly angry at the Agriculture Committee treatment of food aid for the poor.

At the beginning of the sixties the southerners needed to give only a pittance to get the necessary city vote to pass the farm bills. By the end of the sixties the southerners were pleading for a trade with their northern brethern. The seventies opened with numerous northern congressmen talking both about limiting farm subsidy payments (principally affecting the southern cotton planter) and removing the food aid program from the Agriculture Department.

As I have described this political scenario, you must wonder why I neglected to mention the midwestern politics of feed grain and wheat. In fact, wheat and feed grain programs supported by midwestern Democrats, the National Farmers Union, and the Grange have had precious little representation in Congress, particularly in the House where only Congressman Neal Smith of Iowa and a few others carry the banner.

In the Senate, Democratic style farm programs have had a broader base of support because of the sizable number of midwestern and western Democratic senators. But farm programs are drawn in the agriculture committees of Congress, and Senator George McGovern is the only midwestern Democrat on either committee. Democratic style wheat and feed grain programs have been enacted principally because the southerners were trading support. Republican congressional influence remains weakly divided between differing approaches.

To understand the shifting politics of farm programs, I think it is helpful to focus for a moment on two issues which have thrown an unexpected spotlight on the entire agribusiness political community.

First, consider the matter of food aid for the poor. For years only a few do-gooders worried about such programs as food stamps and free school lunches, and even then the program operation was left entirely to the Agriculture Department and its committees in Congress. But over the last three years urban congressmen and the public at large have become increasingly aware that the malfunctioning food aid programs were designed to help the commercial farmer, not the poor, and that the agriculture committees have been most reluctant to reform the programs so they really help feed hungry people.

Second, large subsidy payments go principally to cotton farmers, and on a smaller scale to wheat farmers in the northwest. Several years ago the Senate Appropriations Committee began printing these payments in a book, arranged by state and county, making it easy to look up specific payments. The printing operation was a brainchild of the American Farm Bureau Federation, which figured that existing farm programs would receive a black eye about the big payments.

The printouts made abundantly clear that the most lucrative beneficiary of the farm program was the southern or western cotton planter. Ample attention focused on the $100,000-plus payments for Senator James Eastland, a member of the Agriculture Committee. In fact, more cotton planters in Eastland's home county of Sun Flower in Mississippi receive payments of more than $20,000 than do feed and grain farmers in the entire Midwest.

Finally, attention began to focus on the irony of paying farmers not to plant while at the same time refusing to feed the hungry. In particular, urban congressmen and their constituents began to say it was the Eastlands of Congress who draft the cotton program, who resist food aid reform, and who ignore the hungry poor in their own states.

This all adds up to a Congress and general public which is probably more aware of the agriculture committees than ever before. There is no constant scrutiny to be sure, for agriculture remains a dull subject to be avoided in the minds of most congressmen and Washington correspondents. But there is a growing awareness of the makeup of these committees, particularly among urban liberals who for the first time seem aware that six of the seven Democratic Senate members are deep South segregationists, as are nine of the first ten ranking Democratic House members.

What kind of farm legislation is going to be adopted under this broadened scrutiny? It is still too early to tell, and in the end a short extension of the present legislation might be the congressional expedient. However, it has become fairly clear that a satisfactory farm policy for farmers will have to depend on a new coalition of interests —one that considers the national interest more fully.

The southerners have tried to play their old game by holding food stamp reform in ransom for a farm bill, but the northern liberals probably will not stand for it in 1970, and the Nixon Administration disapproves. The House has twice clearly voted its protest against large farm support payments, and the Senate is bound to follow suit this year or next. A continuing effort will be made to take the food aid programs out of the Agriculture Department and transfer them to HEW and different congressional committees.

Deprived of traditional bargaining devices, farm programs may come to be examined more on their own merits. This process is still extremely difficult in Congress because the agriculture committees remain so unrepresentative of the country at large.

More and more one hears in Washington that "we should be paying people to grow rather than not to grow food." Admittedly, this is a simplistic statement which makes light of some harsh realities of the marketplace, yet it may be a very good omen for the farmer.

As the national population movement continues to move out of rural America and into the cities, the farmer continues to lose special-interest representation in Washington. Perhaps the best hope of the farmer—particularly the midwestern farmer—would be a farm policy dependent, not on the interest of the cotton plantation and textile economy of the deep South, but on the real nutritional needs of Americans and people throughout the world.

HAROLD F. BREIMYER

Agricultural Economist
University of Missouri

5 | AGRICULTURAL SUPPLY
AND DEMAND PROSPECTS

Over countless centuries the agriculture of the more developed world has gone through a slow evolution that can be called its emancipation from the iron grip of the forces of nature. From its primordial state it has gradually emerged into one that is partly subject to the control of rational man. Whether man is yet rational enough to manage it well, and what institutional devices he needs as aids thereto, are the heart of current policy issues in agriculture. But our concern at the moment is not for implications for policy. Instead we want to look at the supply and demand prospects for the new decade that will shape in some manner the kind and the dimensions of policy that ought to be advocated, and might even be adopted.

In primitive agriculture the supply-demand equation was easily described. Supply was the master and demand the slave. Then, supply of food and other products of agriculture was determined by the winds, the rains, the insect plagues, and—some scholars later decided retrospectively—the spots on the sun.

Human diligence as a motivating force was never discounted entirely, but the inexorable control of nature was properly respected. The seer of the age, precursor of the modern secular scientist, saw destiny as immutable yet subject to prediction through occult powers using the zodiac. The mystic, who also has his descendants among us, believed pagan offerings would mollify the gods and modify man's fate.

In such a setting wherein the supply of food was fixed by natural forces, there was no occasion for the mental exercise we now call demand analysis. At most, demand might have been regarded as the minimum food necessary for subsistence. For if man cannot alter the amount of food produced, what reason is there to pattern after Omar Khayyam and try to reduce the data on man's food needs, like his calendar, to better reckoning? But agriculture is now emancipated from all that. We can produce to conform to demand; or so it seems, but the situation is uneven.

Beyond question, the capacity to control agriculture is keener in a technological than an economic or institutional sense. To this partly emancipated agriculture we apply a host of terms. We say we have a scientific agriculture or a commercial agriculture or an industrial agriculture or just a technological agriculture.

The heart of the controllability that exists is often said to be technological know-how. This is the scientist's vainglory. A more accurate view and perhaps a more honest one is that controllability over today's agricultural production is rooted in access to industrial inputs to agriculture that make its productiveness, not merely higher, but more manageable. As their inflow is spigoted on or off, the output of food, feed, and fiber can be enlarged or reduced. Moreover, there is a particular reason why these products ranging from chemical fertilizer to feed additives to animal vaccines are potentially so effective in allowing farm output to be controlled by the decision of man. It lies in a characteristic of agriculture that is so frequently and unnecessarily deplored, namely, its minority status. Agriculture is of such modest size relative to our industrial plant that those industrial inputs can be made available to agriculture in a wide range of quantity. In economists' language they are available at virtually constant supply price.

Having now stressed the potentially controllable aspects of modern agriculture, it is essential to emphasize once more how mixed the situation is, even in the technical sense. Agriculture still has its foundation in production from soil and as such it is still affected by winds and hailstorms, rainfall, and winter freezing of wheat. In the drier areas of the country natural factors are especially influential.

This mixed character of agriculture, its half-emancipation, makes for many complications. We all like our problems pure and unalloyed. Sometimes the industrial character of modern agriculture is stressed out of proportion, leading to conclusions that are specious if not outright wrong. Farmers, particularly the more traditional ones, tend to the other extreme. They often talk as though natural forces still were in absolute control.

For example, if agriculture were totally responsive to control of man, we would not address ourselves to supply prospects for the seventies. We would only inquire into the level and composition of the demand to which supply is to be tooled. In my judgment, agricultural output is now technically controllable enough so that projections of output as a sort of natural phenomenon are not very useful. They are conceptually weak and practically unreliable. We can indeed shape our output of the seventies to conform roughly to demand if we want to. Hence, in pages that follow, less attention will be devoted to projections of United States agricultural output than to estimation of demand.

DEMAND STILL SUBSERVIENT

Nevertheless, even though we are capable of doing better, for both technical and economic reasons we do not even come close to tailoring our agricultural output to fit the specifications of demand. Admittedly, our consumers are no longer totally subordinate to whimsical forces of nature, but they still must stay loose and shift their diets considerably in conformity with seasonal, cyclical, and other fluctuations in the available supply of food.

Notable evidence thereof is a pricing practice that retains for food a fluidity or a variability that scarcely exists throughout the rest of an administered price economy. Only food prices jump around from week to week and month to month. Several programs are now used to stabilize prices a little, among them price support and storage, surplus purchase, and diversion under market orders. But full stability still seems to elude food commodities.

As though to complicate this further, not only do we fret over both realized and unrealized ability to control supply, but we now go to some lengths to manage demand. The principal instrument is persuasion, known as merchandising in the business world but simply as promotion when farm commodity groups try to do it. In addition we employ trade practices, education, and outright prohibition (as of dangerous food ingredients) to shape demand in some measure. John Kenneth Galbraith has built much of his reputation on the efforts and capacity of modern industrial firms to persuade consumers to want what those firms produce and then to adapt the firms' operations to the outcome. Galbraith overstates his case but is not entirely mistaken.

Various commodity groups in agriculture are taking their cue from business and going into promotion on their own accord. They usually do so without blessings of economists who hold as an article of faith that it is easier to promote Serutan than potatoes, and rival promotions within agriculture cancel each other out. But this profession has reaped a disregard that may be deserved, and promotion by commodity organizations seems to be on the rise.

I am not going to build my projections on any guesses as to how well the promoters disprove the economists. For one thing, the debate itself is becoming stale. Speculative remarks on demand in the seventies will rest on three other considerations. They are: (1) that old standby, the buying power of consumers in the United States, (2) the inroads to be made by substitute and synthetic foods and fibers, and (3) the cloudy picture as to export markets.

UTILIZATION OF FARM PRODUCTS

It will be helpful to set in proportion the size of the various outlets for U.S. farm products. A statistical series computed by the Economic and Statistical Analysis Division of the Economic Research Service of USDA is particularly illuminating. It reports the net utilization of all products of agriculture. It is net in the sense that feed crops and the livestock products produced from them are not duplicated. The principal conclusion to be drawn is that domestic civilian food is still the anchor of the farm economy but that exports have been the best growth sector during the fifties and sixties.

In the early fifties, domestic civilian food accounted for about 87 percent of total utilization of U.S. farm products. In the late sixties it has held at about an 84 percent level. Exports (plus shipments to territories) grew from about 7 percent then to 12 percent in the same period. Obviously, other forms of utilization declined. Military use of food was up to 3 percent or more during the Korean conflict and then dropped to about 2 percent. The bigger decline has been in nonfood uses of farm products, down to less than 3 percent from 4 percent in the early fifties.

Total utilization has risen faster than our population growth. Utilization per person is about one-tenth higher than at the beginning of the fifties. The record for exports explains part of the rise. Domestic civilian food use per person is around 5 percent. This is a creditable gain but hardly an impressive one. Moreover, the increase in food consumption is attributable almost entirely to higher consumption of beef, chicken, and turkey. The well-known rise in beef consumption weights indexes of food consumption because it has a relatively high value per pound.

Purchasing Power of Consumers

A generation of economists taught a generation of U.S. citizens that the income consumers have to spend determines their demand for food. We learned that lesson in the depression, when a devastating cycle in employment and income did in fact generate an equally devastating swing in the fortunes of farmers. Later, economists slowly disengaged themselves, and for 10 or 15 years the best forecasters have warned that in a high employment economy the head count of consumers seems to be more important than their gross income.

But economists and public alike seem to learn all their lessons too late. Now we hassle about neither of those chestnuts but about how inflation affects the short- and long-term outlook for demand and price for farm products. In this new concern there are historic overtones. We once regarded industrial depression as typically ushered in by financial crisis. The intense speculative wave of recent years, capped by a conglomerate merger movement that is out of bounds by anyone's standards, is worrisome to any person old enough to remember Samuel Insull. Capital values throughout the economy are full of water condensed from anticipation of further inflation, even though some has painfully been squeezed from common shares. And if we should find ourselves in 1971 with industrial unemployment before we bring the price level under control, we would be an unhappy nation indeed.

To those of us who consistently have been skeptics about the powers of fiscal and monetary policy, particularly the latter, there is a touch of irony in the present situation. For the whole object of redesigning our financial institutions some 60 years ago was to make the monetary system responsive to the needs of the economy, instead of acting as a despot over it. That was the purpose of creating the Federal Reserve system. So we try to reverse ourselves and make monetary policy a control instrument. Perhaps it is better if we fail. Carter Glass may have been smarter than the savants of the New Economics.

These remarks should not be interpreted as a prediction of depression during the seventies. All they say is that one is possible. We would have to declare it more possible than at the beginning of the sixties. To quote Galbraith again, another collapse will come sometime but, as in the case with every apocalypse, we do not know when. In his words, written in the fall of 1969 as commemorative lines, "The only thing certain on the fortieth anniversary of the 1929 debacle is that some day, without fail, there will be another such disaster." And, in Galbraithian irony, "What is necessary for a new disaster is only for memories of the last one to fade and no one knows how long that takes."[1]

There is always a chance that my old economic charts drawn in the thirties will return to vogue, just as my broad neckties have done.

To put this in perspective, let me recapitulate. We have learned accurately that during a slow, rather steady expansion of the economy as in the fifties and sixties, demand for food is not very sensitive to those modest fluctuations in business conditions that remain. One reason is that we have built-in countercyclical devices such as unemployment insurance for consumers and price supports and other stabilizers for agriculture. The second reason is that prices at the farm are less closely tied to prices at retail than formerly, and minor fluctuations in demand may not be transmitted so quickly and sharply as they once were.

But this judgment would not apply to a major recession. A big economic decline would pull agriculture down with it—of that, there can be no doubt.

INFLATIONARY SPIRALS

Our immediate setting is one of inflation. We have seen another demonstration of another old rule: Certain farm prices are quick to respond to the upswing. It follows that they will be equally quick to decline once inflation is arrested. The reason is not so grounded in consumer demand as the equilibrium-analysis school of economists is prone to believe. It is more likely that the difference between the administered price and spot price sectors of the economy explains

---

[1] John Kenneth Galbraith, "1929 and 1969: Financial Genius Is a Short Memory and a Rising Market," Harper's Magazine, Nov. 1969, p. 55.

much about the price behavior we observe. A sizable part of consumer income is precommitted; a large fraction of all prices for
goods and services is so established that they do not, and perhaps
cannot, change quickly. This puts those prices that can and do change
readily on the long end of the teeter-totter. These are food prices
and the prices of certain industrial raw materials.

More could be said about inflation, for instance, how the structure
of the economy affects it. Inflation is being fed, partly by consumers,
but to considerable extent by business investors. Inflation puts a
terrific premium on the possession of property and all durable goods
and stimulates the kind of rampant investment that Joseph Schumpeter
called creative destruction. One consequence is that we get a lot of
statistical indicators of an artificial prosperity. Nevertheless, just
as the peculiar characteristics of inflation make us cautious in our
predictions, they heighten the likelihood that a recession of some depth
may make its appearance in the seventies. The kind of steady growth
we had for two decades does not occasion great danger of cyclical
reversal, but a gossamer prosperity that is built on progressive over-
capitalization of current values almost certainly invites a reaction
that could be rather severe.

NIBBLING AWAY AT AGRICULTURE'S MARKETS

Substitutes and Synthetics

However unsure we are about the likelihood of various possible
trends in consumer buying power, and about how much wallop any
cyclical swings would pack, we have no doubt at all that the demand
for farm products is being cut into by substitute and synthetic goods.
Erosion will continue.

This trend is not new. It began, not with consumers, but with
farmers themselves who substituted petroleum fuels for the hay and
oats they had long produced for their horses. Among consumer foods
there has been substantial substitution. Margarine for butter is the
best known. Now various soybean products are beginning to replace
several foods obtained from livestock. Synthetic foods, those made
from nonfarm raw materials, have not advanced far, partly because
they seem almost invariably to run afoul of pure food laws, as cycla-
mates did not long ago.

On the other hand, synthetics have moved steadily ahead in fibers.
The story is well known but its dimensions are not always appreciated.
ASCS Administrator Kenneth Frick recently reported on the pro-
portion of the U.S. market for fibers held by U.S. cotton, and also
the proportion of the world market outside the United States. See
Table 5.1. [2]

2/ Kenneth E. Frick, "Testimony . . .before the Cotton Sub-Committee
of the House Committee on Agriculture, Monday, Dec. 8, 1969," USDA
(mimeo.), p. 3.

Table 5.1.   Domestic and foreign market for U.S. cotton.

Year	U.S. Textile Market	Foreign Textile Market
1960	64.6%	13.7%
1963	55.7	7.6
1964	54.5	8.6
1965	52.7	6.0
1966	51.3	5.5
1967	49.2	5.9
1968	42.4	5.4

Synthetics have also crowded out a number of other industrial uses of farm products.   These primarily account for the decline in the importance of nonfood utilization of farm products, mentioned above. This irreversible trend ought finally to lay to rest the appealing idea that the solution for agriculture's economic problems is application of the magic of chemistry to developing industrial uses for the products of agriculture.   The depression-born doctrine of chemurgy has run its course.

Still another synthetic displacement is that of urea, which takes the place of protein supplement in several animal feeds.   It is extremely difficult to estimate the magnitude of encroachment by synthetics to date.   Corkern, Poats, and Eley of the USDA have done as much work as anyone.   As a representative estimate, some USDA data is presented in Table 5.2.[3]

Although Table 5.2 includes the word "substitutes" in its title, it relates almost exclusively to synthetics.   Probably because it would be impolitic to stir up an internecine fight within agriculture, the substitution primarily of oilseed products for various animal products is virtually omitted from the data.   That kind of substitution has gone far and has become large.

Nevertheless, for the future the bigger enigma concerns, not further substitution of oilseeds for animal products within the fats and oils complex, but substitution of plant protein for animal proteins.   A USDA report quotes an industry official's estimate that in 1967 soy protein and grits replaced animal-source raw materials to the extent of 175 million pounds.   About two-thirds was in pet foods and some was in calf milk replacers.   But the estimate for meat products replacement was 30 million pounds, and 10 million for soy milk and beverage products.[4]

3/   Ray S. Corkern and Frederick J. Poats, "Synthetics and Agricultural Substitutes in Food and Nonfood Markets," Marketing and Transportation Situation, USDA, ERS, Nov. 1968, pp. 25-28.

4/   Herbert H. Moede, George B. Rogers, Donald B. Agnew, and Lawrence Duewer, "Meat and Poultry Substitutes," Synthetics and Substitutes for Agricultural Products, USDA, ERS, Misc. Publ. 1141, Apr. 1969, p. 34.

Table 5.2. Estimated loss of traditional agricultural markets to synthetics and agricultural substitutes and total agricultural market, 1967.

Agricultural Product or Market	Unit	Market Loss Quantity	Market Loss Value a/	Estimated Total Market a/
			Mil. dol.	Mil. dol.
Cotton	mil. lb.	1,780	456	1,124
Wool	mil. lb.	235	176	385
Cane and beet sugar	thous. dol.	370	76	1,954
Oilseed meal	thous. dol.	358	30	537
Fats and oils for soap b/	mil. lb.	460	31	53
Drying oils for paints c/	mil. lb.	248	32	64
Glycerine	mil. lb.	46	7	25
Starch for dextrin for adhesives d/	mil. lb.	54	4	43
Soya meal and casein for adhesives d/	mil. lb.	76	6	24
Leather for shoe uppers e/	mil. sq. ft.	51	31	491
Citrus f/	mil. gal.	52	45	334
Fluid milk g/	mil. lb.	12	1	3,162
Total			895	8,196

a/ Prices used to compute value were:
      Cotton—25.6¢ per lb.
      Wool—75.0¢ per lb.
      Sugar—10.2¢ per lb.
      Oilseed meal—$83.20 per ton
      Fats and oils—6.7¢ per lb.
      Drying oils—12.9¢ per lb.
      Glycerine—16.1¢ per lb.
      Starch and dextrin—7.5¢ per lb.
      Soya meal and casein—7.5¢ per lb.
      Leather—60.0¢ per sq. ft.
      Citrus--85.7¢ per gal.
      Fluid milk—$5.43 per cwt.
b/ Fats and oils used in soaps related to total sales of soap and detergents.
c/ Drying oils used in paints related to total paint sales.
d/ Market share relationship existing in 1962 applied to 1967.
e/ Market share relationship existing in 1965 applied to 1967.
f/ The market loss in 1967 is assumed to be equal to synthetic drink sales.
g/ The market loss in 1967 is assumed to be equal to known fluid milk sales during November and December 1967. This value is understated since synthetic milk sales and total fluid milk sales are not available.

How much market loss ought we predict by 1980? We probably rely more on intuition combined with memories of margarine, mellorine, and other substitutes than we do on any objective analysis. My own guesses are framed by these two ideas: (1) that we could readily underestimate the rate at which familiar foods will give way before substitutes and, later, synthetics and (2) that food chemists are nevertheless overpromoting their wares. I think we can expect much more careful Food and Drug scrutiny of fabricated foods in the future than in the past. The time required to gain a clean bill of health for any new additive or synthetic food will be long enough to slow the pace of adoption very considerably. My guess is for a higher rate of displacement after 1980 than before.

Export Demand

Of all outlets for farm products, possibly the export outlet has recently been subject to more jumpiness by its pulse takers than any other. Just a few years ago we worried about whether our nation could meet the prospective world demand for our food. Now we wonder whether the Green Revolution abroad will turn our grasslands brown and whether the modest but encouraging upswing in our exports this year signals a recovery or is only a ripple within a new lower level.

We should remember that the almost spectacular rise in exports since the early fifties was sped along by the beginning of Food for Peace shipments. And part of our apprehension about the future rests on the concessionary sales portion of our total outmovement. Will the developing nations want our food, and will we be willing to finance the sale of what they do want?

In my judgment the bursting of the feed-the-world bubble of 1966-67 reflects one of the simplest lessons of economics—the difference between physical need and economic demand. The most abject need is outside the market economy of developing nations and therefore does not affect their commercial demand. To the extent we help fulfill that need we do not affect commercial trade appreciably. Nor does our doing so discourage indigenous agricultural production to any great extent. The stark fact is that millions of people have no way of getting adequate food—not commercially and, still all too often, not from our largesse. Nor is the situation likely to change drastically in the near future. It is because of the persistence of pockets of poverty worldwide that I think we will continue Food for Peace exports for a long time. And the Green Revolution will significantly alter this prospect only when it provides major relief to the nonmarket food needs of local peoples.

Forecasting commercial exports for our farm products puts us back in the same conceptual dilemma sketched at the beginning of this chapter. The developed nations that buy from us have just as half-emancipated an agriculture as ours. No longer is their supply determined solely by forces beyond the control of man; for that matter, neither is demand. And several of our biggest buyers forthrightly exercise control. This is another way of saying that political decisions by our customers will have as much effect as any economic forces as such. Their agricultural technology, like ours, affords more opportunity for political decisions, which are, after all, only one form of deliberate control through the discretion of man.

Forecasts coming out of the USDA have sought a middle ground that was true for a time, and the restraint that steers between optimism and pessimism may be well chosen. Certainly wheat is in trouble worldwide and will continue so. The boom is off for rice. Anyone getting excited about cotton prospects ought to be barred from fore-casting circles. Yet feed grains and soybeans have not yet discredited their more confident prophets. In addition to continuing to ship sub-stantial quantities of food and other products in concessionary pro-grams, we may manage to get a little rise in commercial exports. But the burden will be almost entirely on feed grains and soybeans, and we should be cautious about making it too heavy. So I conclude that our export markets will steer us somewhere between elation and despair.

SUPPLY IN THE SEVENTIES

Thus far I have not presented any summary statistics of supply and demand for the seventies. I tried to explain that neither is a self-determining datum. Rather, both will be affected in very substantial measure by what is done to affect them, and this will be particularly true for supply. The supply of farm products in the seventies will be influenced by what happens in the two arenas of farm policy. These are: (1) who will own and control agriculture and (2) what governmental and cooperative instruments will be made available as aids for control.

For those interested in statistical estimates that begin from certain specified assumptions and methodically reconcile quantifications of supply and demand, I cite various releases of the USDA. A recent paper by Rex Daly, probably the foremost analyst in this field, is worth noting.[5] Daly presents data for 1980, and builds his case mainly on a steady growth in population and an increase in demand for food which exceeds that growth just slightly. He projects an increase in con-sumption of beef, chicken, and turkey and either a steady level or a decline for just about all other foods.

In other words, most projections of this kind are essentially straight-line extensions. As such they are informative. The big flaw is that economic trends do not trace straight-line trends indefinitely. They almost invariably either reverse their course or seek an asymp-tote.

On the supply side, Daly projects a gross output index of 146 in 1980 on a 1957-59 base. That is, total output would be 46 percent greater in 1980 than in 1957-59. For comparison, in 1968 it was 20 percent larger than in that base period.

This too looks much like a straight-line projection. I have no basis for either challenging or verifying the figure although I am sure that output 10 years hence is not predetermined. Yet two elements in the supply picture may be worth noting. One is the conundrum of recent

---

5/ Rex F. Daly, "Exploring the Future of the Agribusiness Industry," paper presented before 25th annual meeting of Tennessee Farmers Cooperative, Nashville, Tenn., Dec. 5, 1969, USDA, ERS.

production response in livestock products, particularly milk and hogs. The puzzle is why production has not gone up more when price ratios are so favorable. Fifteen years ago when I was doing livestock outlook forecasting, we would have regarded today's hog-corn price ratios as explosive. They would put pigs in everyone's parlor.

In economists' terms, these strange happenings in milk and hogs bear on the economics of production response for commodities that are labor using and labor confining during a period of prosperity in both industry and agriculture. When jobs are available off the farm or when a farmer's returns from land alone are adequate for his needs, the response seems to be to desert the cow and the sow. Insofar as higher returns realized by farmers discourage them from expanding their livestock enterprises, we have to defer to a thesis that groups such as the National Farmers Organization have long espoused but economists have scorned, namely, a negatively sloping supply curve.

Incidentally, industrial-labor economists have struggled with the same economics of work and leisure and have developed ingenious explanations such as a spiral or corkscrew curvilinear relationship.

What about the future? If the economy stays at full employment we can look for more of the same high livestock-feed price ratios. If we slip into serious unemployment, livestock production will rise and ratios fall. One other possibility is that further advances in mechanization of dairy and hog production will cause those ratios to decrease. Perhaps. I admit to some skepticism, wondering if the biology of Mammalia will be as adaptable as that of Aves. But on the whole I would foresee some increase in milk and hog production and some drop in average livestock-feed price ratios.

A second element in the supply side is different. It concerns the rampant optimism that we are going to shoot steadily skyward in beef production and consumption. This can happen only if two drastic events take place: (1) the beef cow is induced to give multiple births and (2) land programs will convert excess land to grass instead of idling it. The beef cow is a kept female, agriculture's most expensive boarder. We have taken heroic measures to offset her infertility, but we are about to scrape the bottom of the barrel by grain-feeding every bovine that breathes. The beef cattle industry would probably welcome a breakthrough in calving rates but will resist converting cropland to grass, since it will oppose constantly the pressures to liberalize beef import quotas.

If our economy should go stale, this comment will be irrelevant since demand for beef is just as responsive to consumer income on the down side as the up. But if prosperity continues, the pressure from consumers will become more intense and cause cattlemen to fight a rearguard action. Beef cattle production is probably the least industrialized part of agriculture and the least emancipated. It therefore is the least able or likely to respond smoothly to trends in demand during the next decade.

Who will own agriculture and manage it? How will the developments in ownership and control affect supply of farm products? These are engaging questions deserving separate study. Changes are taking place and they are restructuring U.S. agriculture. Reassurances to the contrary by the USDA and by much of the press are seriously in error. The control structure will not have a great deal of effect on gross production. The economics of instability in agriculture is based on many factors and merely changing the locale and personalities of production decisions will not make much difference. Instead of revamping production patterns, institutional changes will have their sharpest consequences in the way they influence how income is divided among the participants in agricultural production.

WHAT IT ADDS TO

It should be evident that the analyses presented here are far from conclusive. They are a little on the sobering side. Almost certainly demand for the products of agriculture will not be so strong as to give farmers the delicious pleasure of trying for all-out production. The negative factors mentioned, particularly encroachment of substitutes and synthetics plus the ever more free-wheeling productivity that is the mark of a more industrial agriculture and thus an ever more emancipated agriculture, will throw the spotlight ever more brightly on the means that the agriculture of the United States uses to guide, direct, and regulate its productivity. A more emancipated agriculture is emancipated only from the shackles of the raw forces of nature. It is not emancipated, but made subservient to the wishes of the men who direct and control it. Supply in the seventies will not be predetermined but determined, and the question at issue will concern first who will do the controlling and second how it will be done.

HOWARD L. WORTHINGTON

Director
Office of International Trade

6 | WORLD DEVELOPMENTS

The agricultural trade challenge to the industrial world was put quite clearly by the Director General of the General Agreement on Tariffs and Trade (GATT), in a speech he made last month in Bonn, Germany. The Director General said:

> Agricultural trade—the bone of contention in bilateral, regional and international negotiations—must be placed on a normal footing. This can be achieved only if two conditions are fulfilled: . . . if governments take a grip on the problem of production and, . . . if they decide to negotiate among themselves on a virtually permanent basis on methods and techniques designed to avoid their causing injury to each other's trade.

This is clearly the challenge of the seventies—getting a grip on uneconomic production and agreeing to follow sensible trade rules. It was a challenge we foresaw but failed to meet adequately in the sixties.

What opportunity does the seventies present for remedying this? In looking for an answer, several questions arise: Is it possible that governments will move in the right direction without a major negotiation? Is a negotiation a real possibility in the seventies? What kind would it be? Let us explore the last two questions first.

To see the possibility of a negotiation we must look beyond agriculture. Trade policy for agriculture is part of trade policy and foreign policy as a whole. It can be fully understood only within the framework of the broader policy.

UNITED STATES TRADE POLICY

Since 1934 the United States has followed a policy of trade liberalization. We learned from the disastrous experience of the interwar period that attempts by nations to solve their problems at each other's expense throttled the economic growth of all.

Accordingly, during three decades the United States took the lead in the progressive reduction of trade barriers on a reciprocal basis culminating in the Kennedy Round. The result has been unprecedented expansion in world trade and income. Our open trade policy has encouraged international cooperation, the habit of consultation among sovereign nations, the strengthening of institutions for peaceful resolution of conflicting interests, and the rule of law.

Freer trade lowers costs here at home and reduces artificial incentives to the flow of American capital abroad. All countries benefit from the specialization, the growth and exchange of technology, and the spur to productivity that competition in the world market provides. For many years, U.S. agriculture has been one of the principal advocates of trade liberalization, and properly so, for we are the world's major exporter of agricultural products.

President Nixon has reaffirmed the U.S. policy of trade liberalization. Last November he placed before the Congress an interim trade bill to enable us to consolidate the results of the last round of trade negotiations. At the same time he announced that he would create a blue ribbon commission of citizens to undertake a major inquiry into trade and investment policy and to help us design a policy for the dynamic world of the seventies. Work on this commission is moving ahead. Secretary Hardin specifically related the President's policy to agriculture when, in a December speech to the American Farm Bureau, he said, "We are hopeful that all trading nations will work together to create what is truly a world commercial market—with barriers down, prices realistic and less involvement by governments."

We cannot know at this point, whether the United States would agree to or sponsor a major international trade negotiation; but as we move into the seventies, the thrust of the U.S. position on trade is clear. This country remains committed to seek increasingly freer trade, and it seeks to work toward a world commercial market for agriculture. Our participation in a negotiation is not ruled out.

INTERDEPENDENCE OF ECONOMIES

As we enter the seventies, the economies of the nations of the world are more closely interconnected than ever before. Movement of goods, people, and funds among nations is greater than ever, transportation and communications more rapid and widespread, the multi-nation corporation more pervasive. Economic changes in one country profoundly affect the economies of other countries. Agricultural policies of one country result in surpluses or barriers that affect the trade of other countries. One country's efforts to improve its trade balance by restricting imports can be defeated by similar policies in other countries.

In short, nations cannot successfully pursue national economic

policies without regard for other nations. Increasing economic interdependence requires increased international economic cooperation and
policy coordination. During the seventies this will become increasingly
clear, and the pressures to work out accommodations will be great
—another plus for a major negotiation.

REGIONAL TRADE GROUPINGS

The emergence of the European Common Market, the European
Free Trade Area, and other regional trading units was a major factor
in trade policy during the sixties. The further growth of European
regionalism promises to be of even more importance in the seventies.
The British appear now to be moving ahead toward full membership in
the European Economic Community (EEC)—something we have supported for years and continue to support.

With this, of course, will come the breakup of the European Free
Trade Association. Ireland, Denmark, and Norway have also applied
for full membership in the EEC. If the United Kingdom accedes, it
seems likely that these countries will be able to do so as well. Austria,
Sweden, Finland, and Switzerland for various reasons may not wish
to or cannot become full members, but it seems very likely that they
will seek close association, possibly through preferential trade ties.

Spain and Israel are negotiating for preferential association;
Tunisia and Morocco have done so; Lebanon plans to do so. Much of
black Africa is already associated through preferential arrangements.
If the United Kingdom becomes a member of the Common Market,
many of the less developed members of the Commonwealth will undoubtedly seek to associate themselves with the Common Market on a
similar basis. Greece and Turkey are already associates looking to
full membership.

The first half of the seventies, therefore, could see the creation
of an extensive European, African, Near Eastern preferential trading
complex, and this would put severe pressure on the rest of the world
to come again to the negotiating table in a major multilateral negotiation to reduce or eliminate the discrimination it has created.

The trade involved in this grouping is enormous. Our exports to
it alone amount to something like $11 billion a year, roughly one-third
of our total exports. This breakup of the Commonwealth would, of
course, dissolve the present preferential ties between the United
Kingdom and Canada, Australia, and New Zealand. The dissolution of
these ties would have a favorable impact on our exports, and other
arrangements will no doubt be worked out to safeguard trading positions. Nevertheless, I should think that the economic and political
pressures to mount a major negotiation to moderate the preferential
aspect of the bloc would be strong.

I have been speaking of the pressures on those outside this bloc to
seek a negotiation. These pressures should not be all one sided however. These "outside" countries have GATT rights which must be
satisfied. The "inside" countries may find it easier to satisfy them

in the context of a broad negotiation involving additional concessions on both sides.

DEVELOPING COUNTRIES

Trade of the developing countries is lagging. They are over-whelmingly dependent on the export of raw materials, particularly tropical agricultural products, for which world demand has risen relatively slowly.

The developing countries therefore want to get into the manu-facturing business, and there is wide and enthusiastic support among them for tariff preferences in all advanced countries for their manu-factured products.

The industrialized countries are responding. Working through the Organization for Economic Cooperation and Development these coun-tries, including the United States, are seeking to work out a temporary scheme of preferences on manufactured and semimanufactured goods to be extended to all developing countries. Each industrial country has drawn up a preference proposal. These are now before the UN Conference on Trade and Development for consideration by the de-veloping countries.

The U.S. proposal is for unrestricted duty-free entry of manufac-tured and semimanufactured products, subject to certain initial ex-ceptions and to the operation of an escape clause. We seek a common scheme based on this proposition. Before the United States could implement any such proposal congressional authority would be re-quired. The United Kingdom, the EEC, and Japan also have proposed duty-free entry but would impose a ceiling on the amount of goods allowed in at this preferential rate. Over the ceiling the regular duty would apply. Efforts to resolve these divergences are continuing.

Thus the seventies could see the creation of a second major prefer-ential system, in which the developing countries have duty-free access to the markets of the industrialized countries for their manufactured goods. The U.S. views this as one way of doing away with the special arrangements between developed and developing countries—such as the EEC-African agreement, the United Kingdom preferential ar-rangements with the developing countries of the Commonwealth, and the United States-Philippine arrangements. Should these not be com-pletely subsumed in the generalized system the trading world would be further fragmented and complicated.

The creation of such a temporary generalized preferences scheme will intensify pressure for a major tariff negotiation. It is hard to imagine that the industrialized countries would want to maintain the discriminatory features of a developing country preference scheme for many years, but it is equally hard to imagine that they will want its termination to reimpose duties on products from developing countries. One answer to this dilemma is to reduce or eliminate duties for all countries.

REDUCED U. S. TRADE SURPLUS

The U. S. trade balance has worsened rapidly in recent years—from an average surplus of $5 billion in the early sixties to less than $1 billion in 1968 and $1.25 billion in 1969. If noncommercial exports are excluded, we are actually in deficit.

Why has our trade surplus disappeared? The experts do not agree. The boom and inflation of 1966 and the rise in costs and prices is certainly one factor. When our GNP has grown at about 5 percent, imports have grown at about the same rate. Above 5 percent, imports have risen much more rapidly. In 1966 and 1968 they increased by 19 percent and 24 percent. Higher U.S. prices and weak demand in Europe have checked our export growth. The antiinflation program should eventually improve the competitiveness of our exports. The prospects for a quick return to a large surplus do not seem good.

Longer-term trends seem to be changing our preferences in favor of foreign products at the expense of domestic goods. If this is so, we will need to export a much bigger share of our production in the future if we are to regain and maintain a large trade surplus, and there will be increased concern about foreign barriers.

NONTARIFF BARRIERS

As tariff barriers have been lowered, nontariff barriers have become more apparent as obstacles to trade. Nontariff barriers are such devices as quotas, border taxes, and customs practices which restrict trade. In his trade message to the Congress, the President indicated his intent to work to get rid of these barriers. The GATT is involved with this problem, and the preliminary work necessary to a negotiation is going on there.

Thus continued pressure upon the U.S. trade surplus, and our concern with relaxing and removing nontariff barriers will also push the United States toward a negotiation and will dictate that it will cover a wide range of barriers.

A NEW NEGOTIATION?

Considering all these developments, the possibility of a major multilateral world negotiation in the seventies seems strong. It also seems likely that it would be broad—involving agriculture, nontariff barriers, and industrial import duties—with goals far surpassing those of the Kennedy Round. It is not beyond possibility that the countries will try to eliminate duties on industrial goods entirely. This would surely be over a lengthy period of time and with exceptions and safeguard mechanisms, but for industry it is clearly a possibility.

MOVEMENT WITHOUT A MAJOR NEGOTIATION

Is it possible that governments will move in the right direction on agriculture without a negotiation? As things are developing now, Europe certainly will have the opportunity to do so.

For agriculture, <u>the creation of a broader regional grouping in Europe</u> and particularly the accession of the United Kingdom offers another, possibly the last, major opportunity for the Europeans to come to grips seriously with the agricultural policy.

No one denies that reform is needed. Production is clearly out of hand. Three factors support those working for this reform: (1) cost and burden in the EEC, (2) potential burden to the United Kingdom upon entry, and (3) rising concern with the international repercussions of failure to reform.

COST AND BURDEN IN THE EEC

Signs abound that policy planners in the EEC are prepared to take a fresh look at EEC price levels and the complex protection and subsidy machinery which protects them.

Just over a year ago, European Economic Community Agriculture Commissioner Mansholt, principal architect of the Common Agricultural Policy (CAP), offered proposals for dealing with the Community's problem of production and the enormous and growing financial burden it entails. A recent USDA study put the estimated annual cost to the EEC of its common agricultural policy at $14.4 billion. The main cost item is $6.4 billion that consumers pay for CAP commodities produced at prices above world market prices. National agricultural budgets amount to $5.5 billion, and the Guidance and Guarantee Fund outlay accounted for $2.4 billion. Mansholt thinks in terms of reducing the EEC farm labor force by 50 percent, reducing acreage under cultivation, increasing the efficiency and flexibility of enlarged farms, improving marketing organization and methods, and producing less of primary crops and more meat. In his proposals Mansholt is also aiming at bringing farm incomes closer to those of the nonfarm population, an objective high support prices have failed to achieve.

More recently, a French task force was even more courageous in its recommendations for "adapting production capacity to market demand." It recommended bringing prices into closer alignment with the relation between supply and demand and, specifically, making sharp reductions in farm prices for grains and sugar. It recommended that acreage under cultivation be reduced by one-third, notably by removing land from production as fast as farmers working it retire.

Needless to say, farm opposition to both proposals, and especially the latter, was strong. Large budget outlays also would be required to carry out this revolution in European agriculture in conditions reasonably acceptable to the farm population.

POTENTIAL BURDEN ON THE UNITED KINGDOM

Accepting the common agricultural policy of the EEC without change will present a problem for the United Kingdom. Food prices are now lower than those in the EEC and the consumer would find them increased. Some commodities now being imported from outside countries would be produced at home or obtained from the new partners, and this would present some difficulties with the traditional suppliers. Also, the new situation would have an adverse impact on the balance of payments. These problems could lead the United Kingdom to add its voice to those in the EEC seeking reform.

RISING INTERNATIONAL CONCERN

An excellent example of rising concern is found in Director General Long's speech mentioned earlier. In that speech, Long also said:

If a government, or a community of countries, thinks fit to devote, from both the financial and the economic aspect, an important part of the national income to supporting a particular category of producers, that is, of course, its own business.

But when this same government, still with the legitimate objective of shoring up agricultural incomes, decides to produce, at whatever price, products that it could obtain cheaply from abroad, clearly it is shifting an important part of its burden on to the foreign producer; either by reducing and then eliminating its own market's import possibilities; or by securing artificial trading positions in residual third markets, by granting massive subsidies to exports of the surpluses it has helped to create.

The consequences of this situation are serious. . . .

These are sharp words from the Director General of a major international organization, and while they have relevance to a lot of countries, including ourselves, their delivery in Bonn is certainly significant.

We cannot be sure that this opportunity for reform will be grasped, in spite of its obvious attractiveness. There are strong pressures to continue high prices and the established system as well. But clearly, the opportunity is an important one.

IN THE INTERIM?

Whatever the longer-range prospects, major negotiation in which a comprehensive set of new rules would be set is not imminent. How do we deal with the pressing international agricultural problems in the interim? Application of these principles seems sound: It is important that our own commodity and support programs be operated in terms of a commercial world in such a way as to permit our products to compete. All of our efforts to develop markets and to maintain access to those markets will be wasted unless our commodities are competitive in quality, availability, and price.

We must protect and enforce the trade rules and trade concessions which now exist. I wish to stress this point. There is a tendency to believe that no trading rules exist for agriculture. This is not true.

The GATT has very clear rules regarding the inadmissibility of quantitative restrictions, for example, and we must be aggressive in seeking their removal. Over the past year, we have been working with Japan to obtain the removal of quantitative restrictions which she applies to our agricultural products without GATT justification.

In the Kennedy Round and in earlier negotiations, we have secured many specific and valuable trade concessions. We must aggressively protect these. You are all aware of the seriousness with which we viewed the EEC proposal to tax U.S. soybeans. This would have impaired one of our most valuable GATT tariff concessions. On the other hand, we should abide by the commitments we have made to others.

We must prevent others from exporting their agricultural problems to our detriment. This problem can occur in our own domestic market or in third-country markets. We have applied countervailing duties to Italian and French tomato products which were being exported to us with subsidies. We have applied Section 22 import controls to dairy products which were being exported to us under subsidy. We have instituted export subsidies of our own from time to time to regain markets lost to exports subsidized by others or to protect those in which we are threatened.

We must accelerate and deepen the process of international consultation in agriculture. It is this area that will be the most important to us in the immediate years ahead, particularly in relation to the enlargement of the European Common Market. Our consultations must be both bilateral and multilateral.

One of the most promising forums for the kind of consultation in depth of which I am speaking is the OECD Agricultural Committee. This body is concentrating on consultations and coordination in agricultural policies and exploring the long-term need for bringing supply and demand in agriculture into balance. We must encourage this.

The Director General of the GATT has spoken out publicly on the problem we face. We should applaud his initiative and support his efforts.

CONCLUSION

The challenges the world will face in the seventies will be difficult and complex and, for us at least, they will be frustrating. Many of them will be beyond our control. Meeting them, however, promises to be interesting.

EARL O. HEADY

Economist
Iowa State University

7 | PROGRAM ALTERNATIVES

The past decade has been no shorter than the ones which went before it, but it has been so short that the underlying structural problems of agriculture have changed very little.

The nation looked forward with anticipation to the "soaring sixties." Prospects then were that the nation's population growth and economic development would carry per capita incomes and affluence to levels seen only in dreams. Many of the expectations for the nation's economy have been highly fulfilled. From a short period of relative economic stagnation and persistent unemployment in the early sixties, growth and employment were nearly at accelerating rates over the decade. The forces underlying them have become so strong that at the decade's end the overriding national problems have been reversed, namely, how to restrain increases in employment, capital investment, and even the rate of economic growth.

These complex problems, not yet solved, have caused the decade to "turn into a long one" for public administrators and elected officials. But even though it has been so long that one set of national economic problems has been turned into its opposite, it still has been so short and the linkage of agriculture to the national economy has been so weak that the underlying problems of farms have not been similarly reversed.

The forces underlying the problems of agriculture are the same as ten years ago. A decade has not been long enough to raise population per capita incomes and exports to levels where their total demand effect offsets growth in farm productivity and our large supply capacity and translates permanently into upward-straining farm profit. The next decade will be just as short for agriculture—so short that growth in food demand will not offset our large supply capacity. But it will seem long in the sense that changes in the structure of farms,

46

although they may be rapid, will not offset market pressures on prices, costs, and income for the average farmer. It also will seem long as the trend toward fewer but larger farms and a reduced work force will intensify the economic and social problems of many rural communities. This is not a prophecy of doom for agriculture. It is not an attempt to be pessimistic. Rather, it is an attempt to look at the facts and prospects as they exist, so that we can better divert them or build farm programs around them which give farm and rural community sectors a more equitable share in the economic growth of the next decade. Several projections show that with continued trends in population, per capita incomes, exports, and productivity to 1980 we will still have nearly as much surplus food capacity as we have today. Using our current total cropland base in 1980, we could meet our own demand for wheat and have about 2 billion bushels to export—an amount approximating current world trade in this commodity. And a very large increase could be made in the export of soybeans, feed grains, and cotton. The potentials are so large that it's not likely that normal export demand will fully absorb them by 1980. On the basis of projected increases in population (an annual increase of 2 percent in real per capita income—a yearly increase in foreign demand by 0.5 percent) total demand for U.S. food would increase by 2 percent annually—an amount which might be too optimistic if the hopes now being expressed for the "green revolution" in Asia are approximately attained. Even on the same acreage as now, it appears that we can increase output annually by 1.7 percent with practically no increase (0.3 percent per year) in aggregate inputs. Summing all of this still leaves us a continuing overcapacity of around present magnitudes at 1980.

In some ways, it would be nice if these projections were wrong. But I do not believe they are, unless they are too optimistic. I last appeared on the Farm Institute in the mid-sixties and predicted that the "world food dilemma" being posed as an immediate threat would not, as many advocates were vigorously proposing, solve our farm problem in the sixties. Afterwards a few in the audience "razzed" me a bit, suggesting that I was too short-sighted and not sufficiently acquainted with the world population explosion, its imminent translation into need for our food, and the strain on our producing capacity. I believe I am as right now as I was five years ago.

So, what does it all mean? The basic forces of the farm situation have not changed in the sixties. As in 1960, the farm sector could still produce enough to bankrupt a large number of farmers if its full capacity were unleashed in the market over a short period of time. New capital technology continues to substitute for land, maintaining our excess capacity and allowing us to produce much more on even less land, and to substitute for labor, allowing the nation's food basket to be filled with a smaller labor force and fewer but larger farms. In terms of the farm industry's criteria of the sixties, farm programs for income equity in agriculture are needed as much now as then.

While it was known in the sixties, it is now even more apparent that rapid national growth rates, full employment, and inflationary forces have weak linkages and spillover effects to agriculture in a nation at our stage of development and with our food capacity. Linkages that exist have their greatest impact in a more rapid generation of new capital technology which accentuates the decline in farm labor demand, the structural transformation of farms, and the transfer of people in agriculture to more remunerative employment elsewhere. While this complex of forces will surround agriculture over the seventies just as it has over the sixties, agriculture has made some noteworthy progress in the intervening ten years. It does have a set of programs which restrain supply advance and a willingness of the consuming or taxpaying public to syphon a modestly greater share of national income to agriculture. Things are certainly a lot better, from a price and income standpoint, for the average farmer than they would be without the currently effective supply control programs and public-assisted food exports. These programs—while not necessarily optimal and with unequally diffused benefits among the many geographic, income, and commodity groups of agriculture—have removed the very large and costly commodity stocks and have reduced the pressure of large supply on farm income. These are accomplishments which should not be overlooked. Having been attained in the sixties they provide a foundation for moving on to program improvements over the seventies.

There is basic and continuing economic justification for farm programs relating to production, prices, and income for a nation at our high state of economic development, wherein consumers generally are so well fed that their demand is inelastic and agriculture is so advanced that it is like any other industry in being able to produce "beyond" consumer demand. Without programs the continued rapid advance of agriculture brings gain to consumers in the form of lower real prices for food and in the release of labor from farms to produce other commodities and services. But it brings sacrifice to the majority of, but not all, farmers in the form of lower income and submarket resource returns. Yet under appropriate restraints on output, it can be shown that farming can still advance to bring these gains to consumers while simultaneously allowing income gains to farmers. All existing prospects are that programs will be needed to attain these simultaneous gains for farmers and consumers over the next decade if both farmers and consumers want them. A number of programs could do so if they were acceptable alike to all farmers.

Our major instrument of supply control and farm income improvement now is land retirement and the payments which surround it. Land retirement has served this function since the thirties, although it has gone under names such as "the AAA program" and "the feed grain program." It appears that land retirement will continue as the major mechanism to control output and improve aggregate income in agriculture over the foreseeable future. The current administration's "set aside program" is a land retirement program, just as was the "feed grain program" of the last administration. It pays farmers to idle land, so that production will be less and prices and income will be higher.

Not all groups around agriculture agree that land retirement should be used as the major farm program mechanism, nor do all agree that land retirement programs of the current type should be used. Then why do we have such programs? (1) They are beneficial to a large number of farmers regardless of party, commodity, or farm organization affiliation. (2) The consuming or taxpaying publics are willing to support such programs in behalf of equity for agriculture. (3) These programs are a tradition of the past and serve as an "equilibrium," "saddle point," or "acceptable" arrangement for most major commodity, organizational, and business groups within and surrounding agriculture, although they may not be the "first" or optimal choice for any of these groups. In modern terminology they serve in the "context of game strategies." Various rules for game strategies exist and are applied in political theory, in military decisions, and in competitive games or sports. There are many methods to arrive at the best "strategy" or "solution" in these "competitive games." One is called the minimax approach: Two persons or groups are the competitors or players. Each recognizes the "rules of the game" and figures out the plays or alternatives his competitor might use. He computes the "worst outcome" or payoff to himself under each strategy or move of his competitor. Of all the "worst things" that could happen to him under his competitor's "moves," he selects the best. The competitor plays similarly, and the game thus has a given solution for both. The solution does not provide the payoff which is the best of the best, but it is the best of the worst, considering all of the moves that competitors could make. Solutions to such "games" can be worked out mathematically by a computer or by informal methods if the problems are small.

Perhaps that is where we are in farm programs based on land retirement in combination with a few other elements. These programs may not be "first best" for any group, but they may be the best of the worst that many believe could happen to them. If so, because of individual farmer benefits created and consumer willingness to finance them, land retirement programs are likely to continue as the foundation for supporting prices and income for major field crops. Once a policy has been initiated and "bedded down" over a few years, conflicting political and economic interests tend to restrain any important departures from it. These competitions make it easier to agree on and to retain the existing format, with a few slight changes as allowed here and there over time—rather than to initiate an entirely new or different program.

One might predict that not only will agriculture's underlying problem still prevail over the seventies but also the means of tackling it generally will be the same as now. How high prices and income will be under this combination depends on the extent farmers are willing to curtail production and the public's willingness to finance it. There is no systematically organized effort of consumers or taxpayers to curtail treasury funds for these purposes; but it may be difficult to get new funds of large proportions, and there may continue to be efforts to "chip small chunks" from here and there at the margin of farm programs.

Evidently the program committee expected that land retirement would continue to be a major mechanism of supply control and price improvement. Hence, I was asked to review some of the alternatives in land retirement programs.

There are many, and each has its peculiar advantages and disadvantages. Various land retirement plans could be fashioned to attain or maintain a given, or the same, level of prices and income in agriculture. But they also can give different patterns in the distribution of the gains and costs or sacrifices associated with such programs.

The following is a partial list of possible kinds of land retirement programs. In general, the treasury costs of these programs decline from the first to the last one mentioned. Conversely, the social costs, the extent of concentrating the adjustment problem in particular rural communities, rises from the first to the last one mentioned. The list includes: (1) Land retirement spread over all producing regions with only part of each farm retired. This is the program we have had for feed grains, wheat, cotton, and tobacco. It is the "set aside program" being proposed by the present administration. (2) Land retirement spread over all regions but on a whole farm basis. (3) Participation on a whole farm basis with land retirement allowed to concentrate by regions but with some limit such as 25, 33, 50, etc., percent. Each level in allowed concentration has a corresponding difference in cost (with the overall Treasury cost declining as concentration is allowed to increase). (4) Participation on a whole farm basis with land retirement allowed to concentrate entirely by regions of lowest comparative advantage or crop yields. Price improvement or maintenance can be attained by any one of these and other land retirement programs if each is carried far enough. Land retirement alternatives are not of "black and white" and "either/or" choices. They can be combined in any ratio, combination, or proportion desired. We have had three types going on at the same time: the old long-run "Conservation Reserve" from the fifties, a modestly funded "Croplands Adjustment Program" for long-term retirement initiated in the sixties, and the ongoing annual land diversion programs.

Expected costs decline as land retirement moves from a part-farm to a whole-farm basis and from interregional dispersion to regional concentration. The reasons are as follows: When land retirement is on a part-farm basis, the family must stay there and maintain their overhead costs in machinery, buildings, and other "fixed" items. Hence they cannot reduce their costs as much as when they can retire the whole farm and cease these expenses. Therefore they need a lower payment—to make as much per acre as they would from farming the land involved—if they "put the whole farm in." The person who "puts his whole farm in" can take an off-farm job or retire if he is at that age, so that he does not need as much payment for land retirement but can still come out ahead in income from the farm payment and the alternative employment. Similarly, land diverted in regions of lower yields has a lower retirement cost per bushel of reduced production because its output per acre is not proportional to its costs as compared to higher yielding land. Hence if the margin between costs and returns per acre serves as the measure of costs to retire an acre of land, you can get a bushel reduction in output at a lower cost on low-yield land than on high-yield land. You must retire many more acres of less productive land; but if it is actual cropland, the cost per bushel of reduced production is still lowest on land of lowest comparative advantage or yield.

These figures have to do with Treasury costs to attain a given level of supply control and price support. Also involved are the social or nonfarm costs of rural areas which we mention later. These costs tend to be greatest the more land retirement is concentrated by regions, the faster it is put into effect, and the more permanent it is. Even under present programs, many rural communities are becoming so depleted of population, especially young people, that they are approaching threshold levels in providing health and recreational services, in rising costs of public and welfare services, and in the maintenance of established institutions. Ironically, recent programs have generally resulted in rising land prices and growing capital values for farms, but they have not done similarly for other people of rural communities. Physical portrayal of capital losses is everywhere—by former store buildings boarded up and teetering on foundations and by former dwellings with broken windows and crumbling chimneys in country towns over the entire Midwest. Current farm programs have not checked this trend. But concentrated land retirement as well as the speed with which it might be attained would augment this process for communities involved.

To suggest the level of costs of some different types of land retirement programs, we review data for three from the above: (1) The present type of land retirement program on a part-farm basis with diversion spread over all regions—in good as well as poor soil areas. We will call this alternative "present programs". (2) A restricted concentration program where diversion is on a whole-farm basis and retirement is allowed to concentrate whole-farm up to 50 percent of regions of lowest comparative advantage or yields—that is, marginal regions. (3) An unrestricted program where all diverted land can concentrate whole-farm in marginal regions. The data are projections for the seventies, and they all attain the same (real) market price levels, namely, corn—$1.05 per bushel, soybeans—$2.15 per bushel, and wheat—$1.25 per bushel (the same as support levels in recent times —plus cattle, hogs, and sheep respectively at 22, 18.2, and 19.5 cents per pound). To attain this same price level under the three programs, assuming no grazing of the diverted cropland acreage and (aside from present programs) all land of diverted farms taken out of production, the following projected acreages of diverted land are required for 1975:

1. Present programs—61 million acres.
2. Restricted concentration—87 million acres.
3. Unrestricted concentration—96 million acres.

The estimated diversion or land retirement costs (the costs of attaining supply control to attain the price levels stated) of the three programs are:

 a. Present programs—$3.0 billion (land retirement costs only).

 b. Restricted concentration—$2.2 billion (land retirement costs only).

 c. Unrestricted concentration—$2.0 billion (land retirement costs only).

It would appear that regional concentration and related measures could reduce Treasury costs by around a third, considering only costs of farm participation and leaving aside secondary social costs of adjustment.[1] On the latter basis total net farm income, excluding income supplements, would be in the same neighborhood ($16 billion) for all three alternatives.

However, the regional distribution of payments for land diversion would change considerably: payments to Corn Belt farmers would decline from 20 percent under present programs to 9 percent (concentrated in marginal areas) under an unrestricted program, but payments would increase from 8 to 13 percent of the total to the Southeast and from 20 to 26 percent for the Northern Plains. Corn Belt farmers would offset the decline partly or entirely by producing more grain at the same prices, but Southeast and Great Plains farmers would have less land in crops and smaller receipts from the market.

Each program has other particular advantages and disadvantages. At a given level of supply control and prices, current programs spread the burden of the adjustment process agriculture is going through, since—while they do not stop the ongoing move to larger and fewer farms and a reduced farm population—they do not greatly augment the variables causing larger and fewer farms (although some studies show that the current structure of programs itself encourages bigger farms). Their payments add stability to the income of more farmers in more producing regions. But many would argue that, since they are organized on an annual basis, they never actually solve the problem of excess supply capacity and that the public investment being made never actually solves the problem. If payments ceased at the end of any year's contract, supply would spurt and prices and income would plummet.

For programs allowed to concentrate by areas, total costs of programs to attain a given level of supply control and prices would be considerably less than under present programs. They also would aid agriculture of marginal regions to adjust better in the directions they are already headed under current programs, existing market prices,

---

1/ These estimates include that portion of government payments (wheat, certificates, etc.) representing income supplements. They also exclude payments for wool and sugar and conservation payments.

and the decisions of individual farmers. It is in these regions particularly that farms are becoming larger and fewer, even under present
programs, in response to modern technology and shifts in population
and demand. Treasury funds could be used on a concentrated basis
to help these areas make the shifts that are implied in the long run,
as farmers of other regions press forward in technology and cause
the marginal regions to be less needed in crop production—that is, to
be undermined by interregional competition. If organized as long-term
land retirement, through long-term contracts or government purchase
of field crop and/or grazing rights, land could be shifted permanently
(or until it is needed through expanded foreign demand) from crops,
and the Treasury investment in annual payments actually would provide
a "final solution" to the capacity problem.

A long-term concentrated land diversion program would concentrate
adjustment of agriculture on a regional basis. It would not hurry the
process over the major areas of the Corn Belt and winter wheat areas;
these regions would become relatively even more important in the
nation's total production. It might even lessen the rate of adjustment
in these areas because all land would be used and correspondingly
more capital and labor inputs would be required. Merchants in these
central producing areas would be disturbed less or no more than under
present programs.

However, a great concentration of land retirement—and movement
to fewer and larger farms—would be created in marginal crop areas
of the Northern Great Plains, the Southern Plains, the Southeast, the
southern tip of the Corn Belt, and the northern fringe of the Great
Lakes region. While payments, used entirely in these regions, could
be large enough (especially if the total Treasury outlay were held at
present levels) to leave farmers better off than previously in these
locations, the same would not hold true for other persons in these
rural communities. The social costs of adjustment would be trans-
ferred particularly to these nonfarm persons of rural communities,
as the number of farms and workers declined more rapidly. The
demand for the goods and services of local merchants and public employees would fall accordingly, as it already is doing under current
programs and the developing technology of agriculture. The rate at
which these costs would fall on the nonfarm population of rural communities would depend on the rate at which the shift was made from a
dispersed annual program to a concentrated long-term program. If
it was done over 20 years—an annual 5 percent shift in land use—the
impact of the social costs would be little more than currently. A
ten-year period also would cushion the effects, as compared to a
sudden shift from annual dispersed land retirement to a long-run
concentrated program.

Here, in fact, is the crucial element of all social, economic, and
human problems. The facts are that change is not going to stop, nor
do groups at large want it to cease. But at what rate can change take
place, without dumping such large social costs on some groups (for
the benefit of others of society at large) that they become unbearable?

This is a question which we have not yet resolved with respect to rate of migration of unskilled farm workers to cities, changing political configurations over the world, the ethnic and economic transformation of urban sprawl, and the desires of advanced and more broadly educated young people relative to older persons—even in determining how to use rapidly advancing technology as our servant rather than to become its slave. Change can be so fast that it brings unbearable costs with it, but it also can be at rates which allow change to be acceptable. Of course, policies for the concerned groups also can affect the rate of change which is acceptable.

Long-run land retirement programs which concentrate adjustment in marginal crop regions are not likely to be either politically or economically acceptable as long as they threaten to transfer the burden of income depression from farmers and nonfarm sectors of some rural areas to nonfarm people of other rural communities. While long-term concentrated land retirement programs could leave all farmers as well off, they would simply transfer an income problem to the merchants, work force, and public employees faced with reduced demand from a smaller population. This process, of course, is ongoing. Rural nonfarm people evidently are willing to reluctantly accept it at present rates, but they would find much larger rates of change unacceptable. Perhaps the major void in present national policies is that we have, or are initiating, economic programs for the most commercial of farmers and the urban centers. Relatively, we let the problems of rural nonfarm people, small low-income farmers, and persons displaced from farming "fall through the slats." Accordingly, many of our rural communities are evaporating as viable human settlements and economic opportunities. We should turn our attention positively to the people involved.

Another alternative is market-bargained levels of prices, with or without other programs. In some estimates we have made, we find that in a "bargaining program" with prices for wheat, feed grain, soybeans, hogs, and cattle about 18 percent higher than present support prices, acreage of land withheld from production would need to decrease by about 6.1 percent over present programs. If the land retirement and production control were accomplished entirely through bargaining power without government payments as the incentive, farm income would be 12 percent less than under the current farm program with its somewhat lower support prices and its $3.5 billion in payments to farmers. The reduction would be due to cessation of government payments and reduced foreign sales at the higher prices. If the higher level of <u>bargained prices</u> were attained <u>with</u> the present program in force at the same time and with the $3.5 billion of government payments still going to farmers, income under the "bargained program" would be around 13 percent higher than under the ongoing program format.

CONSUMER AND FARMER COALITION

There are many alternatives in farm programs, and many possible

combinations of these alternatives. They have tradeoffs in several
social and economic effects such as Treasury costs, concentration
of adjustment, secondary costs related to nonfarm people of rural
communities, etc. Which should or will be employed probably depends on the desires and agreements of different farm groups. The
competition or "game" over these is, or could be, much more one
among farm groups than among farmers and consumers. As mentioned
previously, evidence suggests willingness of urban society to continue
programs to support farm income and improve resource returns in
agriculture. Organized attempts of nonfarm society to eliminate or
drastically reduce farm programs has been absent and is not in prospect. Of course, representatives looking at budget restraints and
pressures of other social groups will always turn to the possibility
to chip $100 million here or there from farm programs. The "chipping
process" is more likely to prevail than any organized consumer move
to eliminate farm program investments. An example is the "implied
recommendation" from the White House Conference on Food, Nutrition, and Health that "rather than to spend $4 billion for not producing
food, we should spend $5 billion to get food to the hungry"[2] or Sporn's
recent statement dealing with fiscal policies to control inflation: "We
need to reduce our subsidies to agriculture on the simple basis that it
is on the whole in excellent shape and is not threatened by any immediate collapse, whereas our cities are in grave danger."[3]

Still it appears that society at large will readily provide future
programs and investment for agriculture to bring or guarantee market
rates of returns on resources used in farming if: (1) workable means
can be maintained or devised and agreed on by the many farm groups,
(2) payments or benefits are distributed equitably within agriculture,
(3) consumers are brought some "side benefits" from these investments and programs, and (4) the farm public establishes a closer
linkage with the consumer and his needs, problems, and knowledge.
Not only do the past farm programs and Treasury payments indicate
willingness of the nonfarm public to support farm incomes at equitable
levels but they also provide precedent and evidence elsewhere in the
economy. Means have been established, with prices or rates determined by boards and commissions representing the public and
directly aside from the market, to guarantee market rates of resource
returns for such sectors as air transportation, communication,
electricity, and other public utilities. There is no evidence that
society prefers it to be otherwise, even though the process of providing
appropriations and rate changes is usually a set or two behind the
growing population and demand. It does not ask contractors to provide
roads and public buildings at a sacrifice in income on the labor and
capital resources which are the inputs. It guarantees such public
utilities as A.T.& T., Commonwealth Edison, and Peoples Gas

2/   Cf. Des Moines Register and Tribune, Jan. 4, 1970, p. 8-T.

3/   Committee for Economic Development, A Stabilizing Fiscal and Monetary
Policy for 1970, Dec. 1969, p. 11.

Company that the prices or rates for their products will cover the cost of both labor and capital (and it also requires that benefits of technological advances and lower costs also will be passed along to the consumer). In fact the "typical farm" would have fared better economically over the past two decades if it had declared itself a public utility and made a contract with society: (1) in providing prices to guarantee nonfarm market rates of return on capital and labor used and (2) passing along benefits of lower costs from expanded size and improved technology to consumers.

The precedents of society and the absence of organized resistance movements suggest that continuation of farm programs, and even attainment of market rates of returns on resources used in agriculture, are reasonably possible. It would be useful, however, if the farm public exerted a bit of effort to woo consumers in this direction. It sometimes seems that farm groups are one of the few major producer groups who tend to view consumers as their antagonists and competitors. Producers of other commodities follow an opposite strategy. They organize campaigns and studies to learn the detailed preferences of their consumers. They wage continuous propaganda or communication campaigns to convince the consumer that his life and happiness is interlocked with the producer's commodity and progress. But this is quite foreign to the producers and consumers of food, and erroneous concepts and heated blasts frequently are exchanged over the price of food.

Farmers might well borrow a cue from other producers and woo rather than war the consumer. They should be concerned intensely with his welfare where food is concerned. They should try to provide him with maximum benefit not only from food but also in knowledge of costs and returns in food production, processing, and distribution and in "spin-off" benefits from farm programs. They should convince him further that if he will guarantee equitable returns through public programs related to food production, he also can gain from his expenditure. Who should have been the first to discover and become shocked with existence of undernourished people in the United States, concentrated especially in rural areas? Who should have discovered that city school lunch programs frequently provide food unwanted and wasted by urban students because it is not adapted to the preferences of particular ethnic groups or is inappropriately prepared? Farmers and their representatives of course should have, but it was urban people who did. We have large masses of land not needed for food production. But who is concerned about more of it being used for recreational purposes by urban consumers? Not farmers. It is the urban population, hunters, and the Isaac Walton League who must and do fight to get more wildlife and recreational areas set aside from our surplus cropland supply.

This is not to propose that problems of surplus supply capacity and farm structural changes can be solved by eliminating malnutrition from our population and increasing the amount of land for recreation. However, it does indicate both the lack of communication of the farm public with the consuming public and the "opportunities foregone" are using our food and land surpluses to convince the dominant urban population that their investments in farm programs can bring benefits to the nonfarm public as well. An immediate reaction to the discovery of malnutrition in the countryside by urban representatives has been: Why should we make large subsidies to farmers "not to produce food" and let poor people starve? If nothing else, it is poor publicity and inverse public relations.

Modern urban society is highly unknowledgeable about the nature and cost structure of food production, processing, and distribution. It has no knowledge of the share of the retail price imputable to each of these sectors. For all it knows, most of the price represents the farm level proportion. Farm groups should invest in and insist on intensive educational programs to explain the distribution of food costs and the nature of food production and distribution. They should, as Farmland Industries is doing, initiate activities to inform and communicate more intensely with consumers. They should insist on extension education programs carried to urban consumers. Few urban consumers realize that on the average the farm portion is only 37 percent and that the remaining 63 percent of retail food costs represents the freezing, packaging, and other services which the consumer imposes on the final price because his demand elasticity for the latter ingredients. Few understand that this 37 percent of their retail dollar and the Treasury payments they provide agriculture do not cover resource costs in farm food production. Today's urban consumer is so far removed from farming that he doesn't know whether a bushel is an amount which fills a pocket or Central Park. The farm public should extend itself as a partner with the consuming public, warring with it less and engaging more of its sympathy and support through this knowledge and through arrangements to provide it something from government farm programs. There are many opportunities. The nonfarm population could be provided land for recreation, hunting, parks, city greenbelts, and similar purposes through existing farm programs at no incremental costs. The machinery and legislation for doing so already exist, but pressure for implementing and funding the programs at a sufficient level have been lacking. Farm groups could shoulder the burden in seeing that they are, as one step in joining urban consumers in "a great partnership" where both see their gain from government programs. Outdoor recreation is a good with a high income demand elasticity. But the supply per person is no greater than 20 years ago, and the amount per capita using it has declined rapidly. It is unrealistic that recreational land per capita should be static and large numbers of persons should suffer malnutrition in a nation which has a relative surplus of both land and food. Hence there are great possibilities for farm representatives to form an alliance with consumers; to present a view that food production and consumption, land use, and government programs as a complementary set and "pseudo public utility" are for the mutual benefit of all; to use a combination of price mechanisms and government programs, if they so desire or agree, to bring, on the average, market rates of returns to resources used in agriculture, while assuring progress and efficiency for consumers; to provide agriculture with stability and a greater share of the developmental gains of progress to which it greatly contributes but otherwise foregoes because of the large number of small competitive producers surrounded by an inelastic demand and human resources which have low mobility and returns. These are not idle dreams but actual possibilities reflected in the precedents society provides the other sectors mentioned. The course is one which is "well advised," now that food consumers outnumber food producers twelve to one. Consumers have fairly readily provided Treasury support for farm programs, even with insufficient and extremely little knowledge about farming, food costs, and farm returns and the intensity of other social problems which continuously give rise to search for a "stray brick" from here and there to "shore up" other structures.

CLIFFORD M. HARDIN

United States Secretary
of Agriculture

8 | ENVIRONMENTAL QUALITY: THE NEW CRUSADE

The administration of Abraham Lincoln left significant marks on agriculture, for it was during those years that three lasting pieces of legislation came into being—the Morrill Act providing for the land-grant colleges and universities, the act creating the United States Department of Agriculture, and the Homestead Act. Together they set the pattern for American agriculture. The Homestead Act resulted in the settling of half a continent and placed the management of our basic soil and water resources in the hands of independent freehold farmers.

The nineteenth century brought progress and it brought exploitation. The century began with a patent for the first cast-iron plow; it ended with the invention of the gasoline engine and automobile.

Today we are very much aware that technological advances which have done so much for us and for the world also are seriously offending and polluting our environment. The alarm has been sounded, and President Nixon has sent to the Congress a comprehensive 37-point program, embracing 23 major legislative proposals and 14 new measures being taken by administrative action or executive order.

In view of the rising public concern and against the backdrop of the President's new initiatives, it is imperative that those of us with agricultural responsibilities rethink and reassess the special role of agriculture.

As the President said in his message, "The fight against pollution, however, is not a search for villains. For the most part, the damage done to our environment has not been the work of evil men, nor has it been the inevitable by-product either of advancing technology or of growing population. It results not so much from choices made, as from choices neglected; not from malign intention, but from failure to take into account the full consequences of our actions."

Too often we have responded only to crisis. But when we have responded, sometimes the results have had far-reaching impact. The Dust Bowl of the thirties brought more progress in range management and dryland conservation than the preceding 50 years of Great Plains farming. Widespread flooding in the Mississippi basin in 1951 and 1952 brought more support for watershed protection than did a generation of campaigning by conservationists. A five-year drought in the Northeast in the sixties focused more public attention on urban water needs than did decades of talk about possible shortages. A smog crisis in a few major cities has had a greater impact on public thinking than 50 years of steadily worsening air pollution. A few seashore accidents have directed more attention to wildlife ecology than all the voices of all the naturalists since Audubon. Urban congestion and related problems of squalor and crime have brought new interest in the need of people for recreation and open space.

When the first English settlers arrived in America, nature was the enemy. The forests seemed endless and foreboding. Winters were severe. Crops were uncertain. At the same time, bird and animal life appeared infinite. Streams ran free of human waste, and certainly there was no thought of contamination of such great waters as the Hudson River and some of our Great Lakes.

We are no longer a few million people living a comparatively simple life. We are 204 million people living on a major scale. We must plan for another 100 million Americans and the pressures they will create at the same time we attempt to deal with our existing environmental crises. Our responsibility, as I conceive it, is to manage the environment for the widest range of beneficial uses, without degrading it, without risk to health or safety, without loss of future productivity, and without being tyrannized by pests.

Nature itself, without man's stewardship, has rarely been productive enough to meet man's needs—certainly not in the numbers in which we exist today and will exist in the future. Yet our resources must serve every economic and social need of mankind. The challenge is to maximize the productivity of the environment for both necessities and amenities and to assure continued use into the very long future. This requires an integrated approach to ensure:

1. The necessities of life: Adequate food, fiber, shelter, and raw materials for industry.
2. The safety of man: Safe and adequate water, clean air, productive and safe soil held in place, sanitation, disease and pest control, and perpetuation of basic life processes.
3. A quality of life: Space to live, attractive surroundings, suitable habitat for plants and animals, outdoor recreation, and esthetic satisfaction.

The farmer, the rancher, and the forester are managers of an important share of these environmental values. Nearly three-fifths of the nation's land area is used to produce crops and livestock. More than one-fifth is ungrazed forestland. Thus the watersheds that sustain urban America are largely in farms and forests. And the nation must look to the managers of these lands for most of its land treatment as well as management of its water supplies.

The fact that the President, in his special message, made only limited reference to agriculture does not mean that he is unaware of the role of agricultural interests or of the great value of the ongoing programs in agriculture and forestry. Quite the contrary—he was recommending new initiatives and new programs to deal with problems which urgently demand new approaches. While the agricultural work is far from complete, the record is impressive.

Since the Dust Bowl days of the thirties, more than 2 million individual farmers, ranchers, communities, and other land users have voluntarily signed cooperative agreements to put conservation plans into effect. The land involved runs to three-quarters of a billion acres—all enrolled in conservation programs without the need for regulation or coercion.

At the same time, farmers have performed their primary production job so well that Americans take for granted the constant availability of food, its wholesomeness, its variety and quality. Even more fundamentally, U.S. agriculture has freed Americans from what otherwise might be a total preoccupation with getting enough to eat.

Farmers have freed manpower. At the time of the American Revolution, this was a nation of farmers. Even 50 years ago, over one-fourth of all Americans were farmers. If our agriculture had remained at the 1920 level of efficiency we would today have some 20 million workers in agriculture, instead of fewer than 5 million.

Farmers have freed income. Fifty years ago the basic requirements of life—food, clothing, and shelter—required about 80 percent of all consumer spending. Today these essentials take less than 65 percent. So the average family can spend over 35 percent of its take-home pay—instead of 20—for health, education, travel, recreation, and the other considerations that add to life's quality. A major part of this gain is the result of a decline in the relative cost of food.

Farmers have also freed time. Fifty years ago, the average work week in manufacturing was 51 hours, and paid vacations were few. Many things have helped, but you can be sure that if food and fiber production still required one-fourth of the work force, industrial workers would not now have a work week averaging below 41 hours.

Farmers have freed space. Fifty years ago, it required 350 million acres of crops to provide for a nation of 107 million. In recent years we have harvested fewer than 300 million acres. If farmers had remained at the 1920 level of efficiency, we would now need to harvest 500 to 550 million acres, even if we stopped exporting. The acres spared by farm efficiency add hugely to soil and water protection, wildlife, and recreation; these afford land for new towns and open space.

These benefits—income, time, space, and better use of manpower—are enormously important when you think about improving the quality of life. Yet, in accomplishing these things, we have manipulated the environment; and we must manipulate it more in the future.

This involves a whole complex of considerations—natural, technical, economic, social, legal, and political. It involves a recognition that, in agriculture as in industry, new technology has presented new problems in environmental quality. It will require great wisdom to correct these problems, while retaining the gains that have come to us through science and technology.

Some important factors to be considered are:

1. Use of synthetic fertilizers has decreased the demand for manure. At the same time, new farming systems have concentrated animals and poultry in feedlots and other enclosures, creating a problem of odors and waste and in some instances contamination of underground waters.
2. Chemical fertilizers themselves are adding to the nutrients in streams and reservoirs, contributing to plant and bacterial growth.
3. Some of the persistent pesticides, which over the years have saved many thousands of lives, are now found guilty of air and water pollution and appear to adversely affect certain species of wildlife.
4. Siltation is still the largest single pollutant of water. Since the late thirties the silt that has been kept out of streams by the establishment of permanent cover alone would displace a volume of water equal to a ten year supply for all U. S. households.

Because agriculture is both user and custodian of most of the nation's soil and water, the Department of Agriculture recognizes a major responsibility for protecting and enhancing the quality of the environment. In line with this, we have within the past year taken a number of actions to reduce the use of persistent pesticides and to strengthen department programs in the interest of the total environment.

Many DDT uses were canceled last fall, and we intend to phase out other nonessential uses by the end of 1970. We will be taking similar action toward other pesticides that persist in the environment. A determined effort is being made to insure that decisions and judgments concerning pesticides are made in an atmosphere of scientific detachment and are based on scientific data.

Increased research is being applied to biological control of pests, offering much long-term promise in reducing the need for chemical pesticides. Genetic resistance, parasites, predators, and insect disease organisms all have been used with success.

In June 1969 all heads of USDA agencies were instructed to lead a nationwide effort to improve water quality through prevention of pollution from federal activities. The order also provided for periodic reports which amount to a "monitoring" system throughout the farm and forested areas of the nation.

In 1969 130 small watershed projects have been approved for Department help—nearly one-seventh of all the projects approved in the fifteen year history of the program. In addition, the Great Plains Conservation Program was extended for another ten years, and its provisions were broadened to do a better job in pollution control, fish and wildlife improvement, and recreation. USDA planning help has been approved to 12 new Resource Conservation and Development projects for a total of 68 now underway. Most of these projects include accelerated soil and water conservation, development of water resources, and social and economic development.

The proposed Agricultural Act of 1970 would include three long-term crop retirement programs for pilot operation, including an "open spaces" program to help communities acquire land for conservation and recreation.

As we look to the future, the department has before it six major policy objectives relative to environmental quality:

1. Department programs affect at least three-fourths of the nation's land resources. These programs will be administered in such a way as to foster environmental improvement and sustain productivity. For example, all USDA programs will recognize the relationship between soil erosion and water quality.

2. The department will manage our national forests and help private owners to manage their forests in such a way as to provide habitat for birds and wildlife, access for recreation, water harvest, and grass for livestock. These purposes will be integrated in well-managed ecosystems that will produce increased kinds and qualities of timber.

3. The department will strive to reduce pollutants originating in agriculture and to ameliorate the effects on agriculture of those originating from other sources. It will practice and encourage the use of those pest control methods which provide the least potential hazard. Nonchemical methods, biological or cultural, will be used and recommended whenever such methods are available and effective.

4. The department will strive for a reversal in the rural to urban migration that has been taking place since World War II. It will seek to improve opportunity in rural America for all Americans by encouraging community development, productive employment, enhancement of scenic and recreation opportunities, improved housing, and adequate water and sewer systems.

5. The department will strive to help farmers gain a fair income from their enterprises, so that they too may benefit from the environmental improvement that they help to foster.

6. The President has issued an executive order directing that a study be made of all public lands to insure that all of them serve the highest public good. Additionally, I have directed Department of Agriculture agencies to cooperate to the fullest possible extent with local communities in adapting federal programs and facilities to the enhancement of community development.

The environmental job cannot and should not be done by one agency or even by the entire federal government. It requires cooperation with state and local agencies and private organizations. Above all, this is a challenge to individual citizens—those who live in rural America and manage its agricultural lands but also those of all ages and origins who stand to benefit from measures taken there in the interest of the total environment.

Particularly heartening is the interest that young Americans are taking in conservation and environmental questions. We must be eager to accept this energy and enthusiasm and to recognize this cause as one "of particular concern to young Americans," as President Nixon put it.

To some of us who have been concerned with conservation for a long time, it may be startling to find that environmental quality is now a new cause—a new crusade. The challenge to the young people of America is to join with people of all ages in what President Nixon has called "a common cause of all the people in America." This means commitment to a lifelong involvement in the quality of environment.

The challenge to farmers, to conservationists, to scientists and educators, and to writers is to join in a "new conservation" movement that reflects the energy and enthusiasm of the young and the young at heart.

Abraham Lincoln, speaking before the Wisconsin Agricultural Society in 1859, said it this way: "Let us hope . . . that by the best cultivation of the physical world beneath and around us, and the best intellectual and moral world within us, we shall secure an individual, social, and political prosperity and happiness, whose course shall be onward and upward, and which, while the earth endures, shall not pass away."

JUDY FEIOCK

Director, Family Management Project
Corydon, Indiana

9 | PEOPLE AT THE END OF THE ROAD

In many of our rural areas, the scenery is quite lovely, and Lincoln Hills in Southern Indiana is certainly no exception. Roads wind through the many hills and woods. At the end of a number of these roads, in the midst of this abundant natural beauty, live desperately poor people.

Their problems are manifold and include many of the popular cries —poor housing, unemployment, sickness, lack of education. But probably the gravest situation is not readily considered, that of geographical and social isolation. Consequently, we have the difficult task of convincing the residents of each community that poverty in its most depressing and miserable forms is very much in existence in their community; that these are not uncaring, apathetic animals, but fellow Americans, fellow county residents, fellow human beings; that complacency on the part of the more fortunate is inexcusable; that we each have personal if not professional responsibilities for those less fortunate.

FAMILY MANAGEMENT

"My name is Susie and I'm nine years old. I'm the one with blond hair. This is my cousin with me. Her name is Cindy. Cindy has a glass eye since a worm ate her eye, but it looks pretty good. We've been helping mama fix up the house and we worked hard on it all summer. We've patched the house, and worked on the floor and carried out trash and cleaned the yard.

"Mama works in Louisville and she comes home on Saturday night and stays until Sunday. Grandpa drives us down to the bus to get her. She tried to work close by but she couldn't find a job that pays enough money for us. My cousins, my brother and me live in a trailer with

my grandpa. Grandma works in Louisville too. Would you like to
come in and see our new furniture? Mama paid over $400 for it. See
how big the bed is. We can all sleep on it. Oh, that's my brother,
Roy James, in the Batman shirt. And that's another of my cousins
hiding—he doesn't like to have his picture took. Mama bought me
four new dresses for school and she told me to change my dress right
when I get home from school everyday and she showed me where to
put my dirty underclothes everyday so she can wash them when she is
home. As soon as our house is ready, me and mama and Roy James
can all stay here together on Saturday night."

Susie's house is not an exception and such conditions are not limited
to one southern Indiana area. Opening your eyes to similar situations
in your own locality will not be easy but such awakening is long over-
due. Accepting some responsibility for permanent improvement of
these conditions will require dedication to eliminating "man's in-
humanity to man."

Although Family Management is working daily with these problems,
the surface is merely scratched. Important to realize is the vast
amount of equally helpful activities that can be adopted by existing
organizations. The Family Management Project is designed to work
with low-income rural families in the Lincoln Hills area —Harrison,
Crawford, Perry, and Spencer counties. The philosophy of helping
people help themselves permeates every activity we undertake.

This project is federally funded through the Office of Economic
Opportunity and is a component of the Lincoln Hills Community Action
Agency. It is subcontracted to the Cooperative Extension Service
which provides two professionals. The nonprofessionals or outreach
workers are hired and trained by the professionals and their dedication
and skills are extremely relevant to success. The Family Management
Project works in three main areas—family counseling, homemaking
classes, and neighborhood centers. Family counseling is made easier
by the unparalleled rapport outreach workers establish with families.
Outreach workers are not fearsome, authoritative figures, but friends
and neighbors who are obviously sincerely interested in helping the
family to stand on its own. Intensive home visitation is both a vital
and a singular accomplishment of this project.

FAMILY COUNSELING

The A family has come a long way when we consider their problems
of two years ago. The family—composed of wife, husband, and three
children—lives at the very end of a dead-end road, far removed from
the rest of the world. Mrs. A spent her early childhood being shoved
from pillar to post. No one cared for her; no one had any interest in
her. When she married, she had completed nine years of formal
schooling and had never been exposed to homemaking skills. Mr. A
had been reared in a better situation and was accustomed to a cleaner
home. He had, however, long since resigned himself to the filthy
home his wife kept and felt that improvement was out of the question.

The first two visits to this home by outreach workers proved totally unsuccessful. On the third visit the outreach worker gained entry and was greeted by 27 dogs who had the run of the house. Other initially discernible conditions were the total lack of screens, the run-down house and its extreme filthiness, no place in the entire house to sit except on the dog-laden bed, and most especially the social awkwardness of the mother and children.

For many months now, the outreach worker has visited the A's. This is unusual in itself since very few people ever go down this road. All the dogs are on the outside and the number has diminished. When an organization from St. Meinrad Arch Abbey donated wire screening and labor, the A's gratefully accepted. The bed has its first bedspread; a kitchen table and chairs have been donated; the house is about as clean and tidy as possible in its present condition; and Mr. A, pleased with his wife's unbelievable progress, purchased a second-hand sofa and is planning to paper the kitchen. Mrs. A's mother-in-law attributes the improvement to the constructive friendship that has developed between the outreach worker and her daughter-in-law. After all, she is the very first person who ever really cared.

Mr. and Mrs. A are able to communicate with each other better, and the two oldest children are enthusiastic about relating all that has happened in Head Start. Previously Mr. A never allowed his wife to leave the premises. Their improved relationship and her newly acquired self-confidence have altered this. By herself, she was able to take her son to a Louisville specialist recommended by Head Start.

HOMEMAKING CLASSES

The homemaking class series, second of the project's three areas of concentration, is designed to cover ten areas of information during a five-month series. A group meeting is devoted to each of these topics. Each lesson includes academic material, buying information, correct sanitary cooking procedures, storage directions, and recipes when appropriate. The outreach workers who teach these classes use a combination of teaching techniques—visual aids, handouts and discussion, demonstration, and participation by the enrollees. Time during class is limited, and to adapt and reinforce learning, at least ten working visits are made to each member's home during the series. Since parent and child attend classes together, we have the opportunity to involve the children in supervised group activities while their mothers are attending class.

Mrs. B and her husband have lived in a four-room home most of their married life. She knows that the house is in disrepair but the facts that her husband's parents once lived in it and it was originally a school are a source of pride. A visitor must thread his way through a number of partially dismantled cars to reach the house, but he can be sure of a friendly welcome when he arrives.

Of Mrs. B's sixteen children, thirteen are living, nine of them still at home. She is pleased with her children and, like most mothers, eager to discuss them and what she wants for them. Getting what she wants for thirteen children is the hard part.

The interior and furnishings of their home, although old and worn, are clean and in good order. She and her family have participated in every project activity available to them. She has particularly benefited from the sewing she and an outreach worker have done during the working home visits. The family does not own a sewing machine and when she does not have access to the project's equipment, all sewing must be done by hand.

The B family children have been afflicted with serious and expensive illnesses and handicaps. One son suffers from the crippling effects of polio, one attends the Indiana School for the Deaf, a daughter has a serious speech defect, another son has an eye disorder, and the youngest suffers from a bone disease. The B's could have been a perfectly ordinary family except they have had more problems, more children, less opportunity, and less money than most.

NEIGHBORHOOD CENTERS

Neighborhood centers are the newest activity of the Family Management Project. Each county has one center, located in Frenchtown (Harrison County), Eckerty (Crawford County), between Tell City and Cannelton (Perry County), and Grandview (Spencer County). No center is intended to serve an entire county but is designed to reach the immediate community surrounding the center. Programs in the centers vary with each locality. What may appeal to residents in one area could be completely unacceptable to another. Of primary consideration, whenever programs are planned, are the wishes of those who use the centers. The ultimate goal is for the low-income residents to completely take over the operation of their centers. That centers are needed is undeniable. They have provided opportunities for learning sewing, home nursing, carpentry, ceramics, and driving. Mothers' clubs, teen clubs, coffee hours, story hours, and recreation programs are being enjoyed by many. Never before have our low-income people had a facility in which they feel completely comfortable, are involved in the planning, and can afford what is offered. They are organizing themselves and realizing the functions of groups, learning and liking it, and helping others.

CONCLUSION

There is no certain solution to poverty, but there is a certain basis from which we must work if any improvement is to be realized. It is a simple point but unfortunately one which is not easily accepted by many of us—that poor people are human beings. If we should ever permanently break the cycle of poverty, it will require this awareness on the part of the nonpoor.

A higher income and more fortunate circumstances give no one license to be demeaning to a fellow human being. It was on Christian principles that our country announced some decades ago that all men are created equal. It is time for us to examine our principles. We are not proclaiming that all poor people will improve, given humane treatment and an equal chance, because human nature cannot be predicted. Be assured, however, that many strides can be made if attitudes on both sides of the economic fence change. There is a long way to go, but it is a two-way street. Look now at the choice—to take the circuitous road of noninvolvement or to sincerely accept and endeavor to help the people at the end of the road. Robert Frost offers this challenge in better words:

> I shall be telling this with a sigh
> Somewhere ages and ages hence:
> Two roads diverged in a wood, and I—
> I took the one less travelled by,
> And that has made all the difference.

R. J. HILDRETH

Farm Foundation

10 | GOODS AND SERVICES FOR RURAL IOWA

The problem of supplying goods and services in rural Iowa is related to rural Iowa's greatest success story—the development of its agriculture. I know of no more impressive story of economic development than Iowa agriculture. As capable farmers and good businessmen Iowans have evaluated the improved technology developed by agribusiness and Iowa State University. They have used the scientific information provided by the university's extension service and by agribusiness's sales and information force. They have observed each other and quickly adopted those things that worked to improve production. No other industry has made such strides in increasing output per man-hour as has agriculture. Iowa's agriculture is dynamic, productive, and efficient.

But the world seems perverse. This great success story has led to some problems, one of which is the rising cost of providing goods and services for rural Iowa. As the adoption of new technology has decreased the need for human labor, people have moved away from farming areas. Iowa is the least industrialized of the major Corn Belt states, and its rural population has declined more than that of any other state in the region. From 1960 to 1966 population declined in nearly three-fourths of all Iowa counties, although the total population of the state was virtually unchanged. Out-migration exceeded in-migration by a margin equal to about 6 percent of Iowa's total population, offsetting the natural population increase. In fact, a number of Iowa counties have had a natural decrease; that is, more deaths occurred than births.

One way to illustrate the reason for the change in rural population is to look at the increasing number of acres of corn one man has been able to handle with progressively better harvesting systems. Hand-picking with a team and wagon in the thirties, one man could harvest about 40 acres of corn. In the forties with the one-row mechanical picker he could harvest about 80 acres. The two-row mechanical picker of the fifties increased the area to about 150 acres. The four-row corn combine of the sixties harvested about 300 acres. These examples illustrate the process of substituting capital for labor. This substitution has occurred not only in harvesting but also in planting and cultivating of corn. It applies as well to the growing of other crops and livestock.

The average acres per farm in Iowa increased from 169 in 1950 to 219 in 1964. Thus the successful utilization of resources available to Iowa farmers has led to fewer people per square mile in rural areas.

It has often been said that substitution of capital for farm labor and purchase of more inputs from off the farm leads to an increase in off-farm agribusiness. The evidence seems to support this contention. For example, in 1950 when cash receipts in Iowa amounted to $2.1 billion and production expenses were $1.4 billion, net cash income was 35 percent of cash receipts. But in 1968 when cash receipts were $3.5 billion and production expenses were $2.8 billion, net cash income was only 18 percent of cash receipts. This narrowing of the margin of profit was due to the increase in off-farm inputs that go to make a corn crop or to get a hog to market weight. These data appear to indicate that the population of Iowa will not decline, that people working in off-farm agribusiness will increase and balance out the decline in farmers.

Why then has the population of three-fourths of the Iowa counties declined? First of all, many of the off-farm agribusiness inputs are not supplied in the same county in which they are purchased. They are manufactured in large cities and distributed from trade centers. Iowa farmers are also not the only ones who have improved their efficiency —the off-farm agribusiness industry has improved its efficiency as well. It was estimated in the fifties that agribusiness accounted for roughly 30 percent of the economic activity in the nation. A recent study by the Federal Reserve Bank of St. Louis indicates that agribusiness now comprises only about 20 percent of the nation's economic activity.

The conclusion is inescapable: the successful economic development of farming and agribusiness is a major reason for the shrinking rural population in Iowa.

Now, let us turn to the impact of fewer people per square mile on the costs of public and private services. I grew up in Story County and still have many relatives and friends there. As we get together to visit and our conversation turns to the prices of the things we buy, I come away with the feeling that it costs more to live in rural Iowa than it does in the suburb of Chicago where I now live. One major exception to this might be the cost of housing. But the costs of food, clothing, fuel, household supplies, and other items seem higher in rural Iowa. Why is this? The answer may lie in the concept of certain fixed or overhead costs in providing both public and private goods and services to people. As the population per square mile is reduced, the

costs of distributing these goods and services rise very rapidly because
the fixed overhead costs are spread out among fewer people.   For
example, consider a rural church. If it has an adult membership of
1,000 persons and the cost is $20,000 for lights, heat, repairs, and
the minister's salary, the cost per adult member is $20.   If this
congregation drops to 500 members the cost per member is $40, and
if it shrinks to only 100 members the cost per member is $200.

Whether or not a local rural congregation is in financial difficulty
probably depends a great deal more on the willingness of the members
to make contributions than the underlying concept of fixed costs for
operating the church. However, the economic relationship is there,
and if the membership drops sharply, the per person costs do rise
very rapidly. The same sort of relationship holds for schools, county
and township government, medical facilities, food stores, hardware
stores, and clothing stores—all the institutions and firms that provide
goods and services, both public and private.

The proposed "farm shopping centers" represent a reaction by
private industry to high per customer fixed costs. The concentration
of several supply and marketing firms at a single "farm shopping
center" is expected to draw enough customers to lower the per customer fixed cost at the retail level. The costs of distribution for the
merchandiser will also be lower, since larger stores in fewer centers
can be serviced more efficiently than smaller stores scattered throughout many towns. The promoters of the "farm shopping centers" think
the reduction in costs will be sufficient to pay for the construction of
new facilities and still return a profit. If their expectations are correct, many small towns and even some larger ones will face severe
adjustment problems.

What, then, are the alternatives facing rural Iowa with regard to
this problem of the rising cost of goods and services? I do not think
an acceptable alternative is to go back to the team and wagon, the
bang board, and handpicking of corn. After all, Iowans are in competition with other areas of the Corn Belt. Corn is also in competition
with other feed grains. The alternative of returning to old farming
methods with greater labor needs and higher population per square
mile is hardly the answer.

A second alternative is to lower the quantity and quality of public
services. In a declining population the same amount of taxes per
person can only provide for less service or services of a lower quality.
If the number of farmers is considerably smaller and each farmer
pays the same amount of taxes as in the past, the amount of education
offered in the schools will have to be reduced or be of inferior quality.
The same holds true for county government, public health, and fire and
police protection.

Iowa, by and large, has not chosen this alternative. It has in effect
chosen a third course. The information I receive indicates that in the
main, Iowa has maintained reasonably good school systems and government services, but taxes per person have been rising. Taxes are
becoming so high that some contend that the quantity and quality of

public services are better than they can really afford. To continue down this road of maintaining good public services will require even higher taxes.

Iowa can decide to put a larger percent of income into schools and other government services and a lower percent into cars, clothes, vacation trips, and other consumer goods. The tax burden can be eased by another round of consolidation—of schools and of other governmental units. Regional planning to provide public health care, post-high-school education, and other public services on a basis of units larger than a county could also lower costs. But all of this is speculative. It is becoming increasingly difficult to provide public services in areas where population is declining. For example, I find curious parallels between rural areas with a declining population and urban ghettos. It takes more money to obtain the services of professional people in both places as compared to suburbs. Professional people want professional and cultural opportunities and stimulation and say they do not find them in ghettos and small towns. The prices of things they want to buy are lower, and many think schools and other public services are better in the suburbs. For this and other reasons, the maintenance of adequate public services for a dwindling rural population will be difficult and costly.

A major alternative to the possibilities already discussed is to increase the rural population for reduction of the fixed cost per capita of public and private goods and services. How do you get more people to live in rural Iowa? There are a number of ways, and some have been tried. For example, one way is to put retirement homes out in the country. Another is to put government institutions such as orphanages, hospitals, etc., in rural areas. However, these types of developments offer only limited potential.

The major way is to create more jobs in rural areas or nearby urban areas. For example, the areas surrounding Des Moines, the Quad Cities, and Cedar Rapids have not had as severe a problem as some other parts of rural Iowa, for instance, between Des Moines and Council Bluffs or southern Iowa, because of the growth of jobs in nearby metropolitan areas. People live in the country and commute to their jobs. This phenomenon, incidentally, shows that it will not be possible to have uniform growth over all of rural Iowa at the same time. Those areas surrounding places where jobs are increasing will develop faster than those farther away.

It is possible that Iowa should adopt a strategy of increasing its population. By the year 2000 we are going to have to find a place for another 100 million people in the United States. Take it from a fellow who lives in the area, squeezing Chicago's portion of this new 100 million people into the present geographic area of Chicago is going to present some monumental problems. We already have serious problems of congestion, air and water pollution, and other difficulties of crowding. The addition of a large number of people will certainly lower the quality of my life and those who now live in the Chicago area. Approximately 10 million people are now living on the strip of land extending from Milwaukee around the southwest and south shores of

Lake Michigan. Putting another 5 million people in that area is going
to cause very great problems. In fact, most of the major metropolitan
areas of the United States may not be able to deal with population increases of any sizable proportion. So if Iowa were to adopt a strategy
of rural development to attract people, it could make a major contribution to the quality of life in the nation as well as the quantity and
quality of public and private services at a reasonable cost.

Still another reason for opting for the economic development of
rural Iowa is the possibility of a second pay check for you and your
family. If jobs are available to more rural people in Iowa, many could
find off-farm employment. Such an opportunity could ease the adjustments required as new farming technology continues to reduce the
number of people needed in agriculture. If nonfarm jobs are not available, the young people will continue to leave and the population will
continue to decrease. I realize Iowa cannot increase its population
on its own. National policy will have to be formulated to redistribute
population. But even with a positive national policy, Iowa will have
to make the decision of working or not working with it.

The choice of options is up to Iowa residents. They can choose to
have lower quality public services and pay more for private services,
pay more for both public and private services, or adopt a definite
strategy of attempting to increase the population of rural areas.

But more than Iowa's share of the 100 million people will not come
to rural areas just because they are wanted. Suggesting steps for
bringing more jobs to rural Iowa is very difficult. It is a complex
job with many ramifications, which cannot be covered here.

The same sources that have helped in Iowa's successful job of
economic development of farming can assist in this new job. University research and extension facilities can be of great assistance.
The business communities and the chambers of commerce can help.
Government agencies at the state and national level can assist, as they
have in the job of agricultural development.

But just as Iowans must face adjustments in the way things are
done, so must chambers of commerce, government, and universities.
Rural Iowa has a hodgepodge of small fragmented institutions and
services scattered inefficiently. They were useful for the technology
of 50 years ago but are ill-suited for today's technology and today's
world. Until rural people and public and private agencies and organizations can think and plan on the basis of the larger community, there
may be no alternative but to face the fact of mounting costs and low
quality goods and services.

If chambers of commerce cannot think and plan on the basis of the
larger community, little will happen. Rural people will have to work
together. It will take group action to accomplish rural economic
development. One farmer can make a decision to adopt new technology
and move on that decision. But in the process of rural development a
number of people will have to work together to lead the larger community toward a definite decision and its implementation. This will be
infinitely more difficult and more time consuming, but even here there

is a science and technology of human relationships that can be learned and used.

If Iowa is successful, the costs of public and private services will be lowered. New people with new ideas will be neighbors. They will have new and different ways of thinking and their own way of doing things. They will disrupt established ways. New firms and businesses will compete with the present ones. Those who are comfortable with the way things are now may feel disturbed. Some capital may have been invested; it will not all come from out of the state. Rural Iowa will likely be a more exciting and interesting place to live.

So I suggest Iowans begin to ask questions and think about the possibilities of how rural areas might make a contribution to the quality of life, to the total nation, and also to lower costs for public and private services by creating an environment that will attract more than the present amount of the 100 million people that will need to be placed somewhere in this country by the year 2000.

This task should not frighten those who have been willing to think about new ways of growing corn and hogs and who are actually growing corn and hogs in ways that their fathers would not recognize or understand.

CHARLES P. GRATTO

Economist
Iowa State University

11 | WATER, AIR, AND LAND QUALITY

Quality is measured by some standard. That standard may be a content standard. I might say "this tire is of higher quality than another because it has 10 percent more rubber in it; this gasoline is of higher quality than another because it has 10 percent fewer impurities in it." Or quality may be discussed in terms of performance. "This tire is of higher quality because it will last 20,000 miles under normal use while others will last only 10,000 miles; this gasoline gives 20 miles per gallon in the average car, that gasoline gives only 16 miles per gallon."

We can apply the same kind of reasoning to our physical environment. For example, "this environment has a lower quality now than ten years ago because it contains fewer forms of plant and animal life than it used to. The quality of this environment is lower than it used to be because it contains more junked cars and old refrigerators." Thus we can judge the quality of our environment, or a part of it, —like air, land, or water—by measuring what it contains against what it should contain.

Or, we can apply performance standards to our environment. "This environment is not performing as well as it once did, it is not reproducing itself; this watershed is not performing well enough, soil is eroding out at twice the rate that is reasonably acceptable." So, standards are what we expect of our environment or a part of it; standards let us measure environmental quality.

What do we expect of the environment or part of the environment? As far as performance goes, we expect the environment to remain in dynamic equilibrium, that is, in balance through time. We want all parts of the environment to retain the capacity to regenerate and to cleanse themselves. We want all parts of the environment to be in balance. We would like to survive, and we would like the natural environment as we know it and value it today to survive with us.

76

Performance standards are related to content standards. We measure numbers of E. coli in water to see if water can perform (or be used) in a certain way. We measure radiation on land, particles in the air, and pesticides in the food chain for the same reason. The content standards we apply to the environment let us measure its condition and see if it is performing in such a way as to reach or remain in a state of dynamic equilibrium.

We demand high standards in our environment because we have an advanced technology, we have a large gross national product and wish to be healthy. At the same time we are putting great pressure on the environment. Good health, high income, and advanced technology cause an enormous dislocation of resources as we operate now. Production and consumption of the kind we have now create great quantities of waste materials. We would like to throw away waste and be done with it. But where is "away"?

If we pour matter and energy into the environment faster than it can be used up or destroyed by the many possible physical and biological processes, it will accumulate. That accumulation threatens two things. First, it threatens content standards for air, water, land, living space, and organisms, including man. When content standards are not met, production and consumption of the things we all want are more costly, they are curtailed, or both. Content standards for health, safety, cleanliness, quietness, and beauty are violated by accumulation of waste matter and energy; and each violation brings with it a penalty to the human organism. Second, the accumulation of waste in the environment can throw the whole system out of balance. Parts of the environment lose their capacity to cleanse or regenerate themselves; they break down and cease to function. Their function must be taken over by some other environmental component or not be accomplished at all. The least penalty for overwhelming a part of the environment must finally be a higher cost for goods and services. Some scientists predict far graver results.

Air, water, and land can be thought of as spaces to put matter and energy we no longer want. Each of these spaces is measurable. Each is finite. There is known and fixed space that is our atmosphere. There is known and fixed space that is occupied by water. There is known and fixed space that is occupied by land. As energy and matter are placed in these spaces, the energy is dissipated and the matter is broken down by physical and biological processes.

As unromantic as it sounds, air, water, and land function as large, finely balanced, sometimes fragile, waste disposal machines. Even if there were no people these would function to process natural waste. Each space—air, water, and land—seems to have an excess capacity that until recent time has been able to accommodate most man-made waste. It would be folly not to use this excess capacity for waste disposal since it is in effect a free good. It would be a greater folly to overuse the waste disposal capacity since this would destroy a free good and cause us to spend money to perform the same function. But economic theory tells us that free goods are always misallocated.

How are we doing with the air, water, and land space? Let me sketch in a very general way the status of these resource spaces.

Soil receives radiation, pesticides, and herbicides, plus solid waste and garbage in landfill operations. Radiation poses no hazard provided there are no further above-ground nuclear explosions. Some of the herbicides and pesticides degrade quite rapidly and pose no threat, but others degrade very slowly and until the weight of scientific evidence says otherwise, pose a real problem. Land can handle some junk and garbage, but space is short in many areas having large, concentrated populations; and the production of solid waste doubles in less than 20 years. We must conclude that as far as land is concerned we are using up the excess cleansing or regenerating capacity at a rapid rate. In some cases local capacities have been overwhelmed.

The resource space called water includes the sea, estuaries, lakes, rivers, groundwater, and surface water. Materials dumped in water often end up in the sea. There is no evidence that the sea as a whole is suffering as the result of an accumulation of waste matter and energy. Notable local accumulations, oil slides and heat for example, do show up and cannot be lightly dismissed.

Lakes are small-scale, freshwater versions of oceans. They can be overwhelmed by too rapid plant growth from changes in nutrient levels due to fertilizers, by toxins of all varieties from many sources, by silt, and by organic waste. Some lakes, large and small, have lost their capacity to regenerate themselves.

Estuaries are the places where freshwater and saltwater mix. They are fragile biologically and physically. They are under great pressure because they are on the coasts where there are large concentrations of people and resources. Some estuaries have been filled in, and some are unable to regenerate themselves.

A river can cleanse itself if it is not overloaded. However, many rivers have been subjected to a great accumulation of waste products and have lost their capacity for regeneration. Others are being pushed to the limit. Sources of matter range from human waste through exotic toxins from sophisticated industrial and agricultural activities.

Groundwater can also receive and hold waste material, since it is connected to surface water and rivers through a series of complex hydraulic relationships. Some groundwater reservoirs have accumulated undesirable levels of waste matter, others are likely to do so.

Surface waters are like a tiny version of lakes and rivers. They can be and often are overwhelmed by nearby sources of waste matter and energy.

In summary, part of the self-cleansing ability of the water resource has been lost, part has been impaired, and part is endangered. Water is a resource space whose management requires the most careful attention.

The total climate system, the resource space called air, is very large. It is not well explored or mapped. Exotic substances such as carbon dioxide, radiation, aerosols, and particles of many kinds have been introduced into the system, and their ultimate impact remains uncertain. Concentrations of matter and energy occur because air masses move slowly and temperature inversions occur. These phenomena sharply reduce the available air space, while emission of energy and matter are not proportionally reduced. Such concentrations have results that range from annoying to lethal. We are uncertain about the ultimate effects of placing waste in the atmosphere and have already experienced localized shortages of air space.

It appears that a vast management process is in order to balance off the rate at which our society places matter and energy in air space, land space, and water space with the rate at which matter and energy can be dissipated in these spaces.

The management of our environment clearly has emerged as a public policy issue. Rural people are caught up in the resolution of the issue of how best to manage our air, water, and land resources and will be deeply involved for the forseeable future.

We live in an interdependent society. Just as all the people of the nation are invisibly linked together in the production and consumption processes that are tallied in our GNP, so they are linked together by a set of ecological forces that must be balanced by the physical environment. Just as we all suffer when the economy is distorted by inflation or depression, so we all pay penalties when environmental forces are unbalanced by accumulated waste. Because agriculture rests on a highly sophisticated technology, it has great potential for discharging large quantities of waste material into the environment spaces—air, land, and water. Because it relies on living organisms in production, it is vulnerable to the effects of waste accumulation.

Rural people, indeed all the people of the nation, need to give more thought to managing the environment. As they do so, some choices are open. The first is to proceed as we are, on the assumption that things will work out or that at some critical moment a technological breakthrough will serve to bail us out of any crisis that develops. The advantage is that this involves a minimum of adjustment. The disadvantage is that this strategy does not take uncertainty into account. Businesses that do not do this ultimately pay a high price for the omission. Common sense indicates that societies failing to adjust to uncertainty must finally pay a price of some unknown amount.

A second choice is to proceed as we are, recognizing that we are acting without full knowledge of the ultimate effect. This course would involve making adjustments for many contingencies, some of which may in the end never occur, some of which may not be as serious as expected. It is a course of caution, with the assumption of higher costs now against an unknown future payoff.

A third option is to speed up our learning about the environment so that we can move from uncertainty to risk. The more we know about the environment, the better decisions we can make. If we could learn fast enough, the management of our environment could be carried on in a rational way.

The grand strategy for treating environmental questions through the seventies and beyond will contain elements of the three choices sketched above. The big environmental problem is made up of many specific situations that will have to be resolved one at a time. In each case there will be a resource space, an accumulation, and a difference between an existing and desired standard. The solutions found for each specific case will involve changes in how people live and work, and the resolution of issues in quality of environment will not be easy or simple.

Success in solving the big problem of quality of environment in rural America can only come by finding correct lines of action in each of the multitude of specific issues. Just as the problem emerges from many cases of unwanted accumulation, the solution will be found by reducing those accumulations one at a time by economic, social, and physical changes.

Every rural family is involved in the issue of quality of environment. If each acts to solve the problems near his home and in his community, we can expect to end the decade with an environment better than we find it today.

SAMUEL C. JACKSON

Assistant Secretary for
Metropolitan Development

12 | BUILDING URBAN CENTERS IN RURAL AMERICA

The National Farm Institute has been taking a long, hard look at the many facets of our total domestic picture. Since 1937 the Institute has been discussing problems relevant to the rural community. At the beginning of a new and complex decade, it is significant to be dealing with the intricate relationships between the rural community and its urban counterpart. It is my hope that the ideas and theories developed at this Institute will have a profound effect on our efforts at domestic problem solving.

Some years ago the father of this atomic age, Albert Einstein, was asked to outline one of his most abstract and complicated theories in simple terms.

He explained it this way: When you sit with a nice girl for two hours, you think it's only a minute. But when you sit on a hot stove for a minute, you think it's two hours. That is relativity.

As one who has occupied a hot seat in Washington for the past year, I can assure you I have developed a greater understanding of and a much deeper appreciation for Einstein and his theories. In a way, Einstein's theories have a great deal to do with what has been done, and what will be done in the future in attacking the problems we find in such abundance in our cities, our suburbs, and our rural communities.

It depends very much upon where you are sitting how you see the problem and how much time and effort you want to put into its solution. We also begin to see, as Einstein outlined in another of his theories, that time is not simply an added ingredient in a problem, it is a dimension as important as the length, the width, and the depth of the problem in finding its solution.

We can hardly pick up a magazine or a newspaper or watch a television newscast without noting some reference to the crisis of our cities, the crisis of our suburbs, or the crisis of our rural communities.

Generally, the conditions depicted are bad, very bad. Unfortunately, they are also generally accurate. We do have massive problems in many if not all our central cities; we do have growing problems in our suburbs; and while the news media appear to be just now discovering the depth of the problems in rural communities, they are no less serious than those in our central cities and their adjacent areas.

Our domestic problems have been in many instances by-products of the great successes of this nation. Technology in America has advanced and improved almost unbelievably. But with the technological progress—development of the modern and superproductive factories in this country—has come the pollution of our environment.

The United States is the most affluent nation in the world today. Many people have better homes, better jobs, and more money to spend than ever before. But this affluence is not shared by all, and the problems of economic and racial segregation have become greater.

We can see how the great successes of the American people can, if they are not dealt with carefully, become one of the causes of our great domestic problems.

Let us take a look at our problems—the problems of the cities, the problems of the suburbs, and the problems of our rural communities. What are the problems of our cities? There is, of course, the physical deterioration of homes, of schools and other public facilities, of commercial centers, and of industrial plants which have grown obsolescent and inefficient. There is the movement of middle and higher income families to the suburbs, leaving behind ghettoes—often black ghettoes—of low-income families. Industry and business often join this movement of higher income groups to the suburbs, taking with them a great deal of the ability of the central city to finance and improve conditions because of erosion of the local tax base.

The suburbs of many of these central cities are also having problems. They are finding it increasingly difficult to provide the services necessary to serve burgeoning populations. High land acquisition costs, rapidly mounting construction costs, high interest rates, and local debts pushing state limits have all but stopped new school construction in many rapidly growing areas. Meanwhile, that great gray area of urban sprawl continues to spread outward over thousands upon thousands of acres of land, using up resources, spreading erosion and pollution, compounding traffic congestion, and using up prime agricultural land in massive chunks with what appears to be a relentless appetite.

We also know what has happened and is happening to many of our rural communities. Many of them have lost population, or at least they are not growing. Part of the reason has been the success, not the failure, of the rural community. If there has been one revolution that has really worked, if there has been one segment of our population that has done more than it was asked to do—and then some—it has been the agricultural community.

The revolution in farm production has meant a great deal to our nation and the world in better nutrition and hope for the future for millions. Communities, especially smaller ones, in largely agricultural areas have often been victims of their own success.

As farms became more and more mechanized and scientific, fewer and fewer people were needed to run and manage them. Television brought the world into the farmer's living room, and interstate highways and the airplane allowed him and his family to get out into it. His relatively greater prosperity sent his sons and daughters to college and, after college, to the big cities. They married, began to raise families, and headed back toward the farm, but they never got there. They stopped on the way and bought a home in the suburbs.

The result is easily observable on any weekday morning in any large city in the United States. There is a glut of automobiles inching their way into the central city along superhighways designed to handle sixty-mile-an-hour traffic, fighting for almost nonexistent parking spaces, or paying outlandish prices for them, to go to work in relatively high-paying jobs in the downtown area.

Meanwhile, an army of automobiles almost as great, moves from the central city into the suburbs. They are filled with workers to man the new industries and commercial establishments moving with such increasing frequency to the outskirts of our big cities.

I have outlined conditions as we find them today in our cities, our suburbs, and our rural communities. Unfortunately, as bad as they are, they are going to get worse if we continue to do things the way we have been.

When we look down what science writers like to call the space-time continuum, we find things getting more complicated. In the first place, we are going to have more people in the future, a lot more people. Our total population is growing at the rate of better than 1 percent a year. This means we will add another 100 million to our present population by roughly the year 2000, only 30 years away. If this additional 100 million people were divided equally between our cities, our suburbs, and our rural areas, our problems would be difficult, but probably not unmanageable. However, all the information we have indicates that this will not be the case. If present trends continue, about 85 percent, or 85 million, will concentrate in the 12 major existing urban regions of our nation—regions already overcrowded, already suffering from hardening of transportation arteries and running as fast as they can simply to stand still.

In his 1970 State of the Union message, President Nixon talked about these problems of our cities, our suburbs, and our rural communities, not as separate pieces, but as part of an entity. He proposed the creation of a national growth policy for the purpose of "finding those means by which Federal, State and local government can influence the course of urban settlement and growth so as positively to affect the quality of American life. In particular," the President stated, "the Federal government must be in a position to assist in the building of new cities and the rebuilding of old ones." Further, President Nixon said, "what rural America needs most is a new kind of assistance. It needs to be dealt with, not as a separate nation, but as part of an overall growth policy for all America. We must create a new rural environment that will not only stem the migration to urban centers, but reverse it. "

None of us can argue with the fact that what the President seeks —and the policy to which he has committed his administration—is basic, comprehensive, and essential.

Too often federal programs and policies in past administrations have been attempts to stick fingers in dikes where no dikes existed. The result has been inefficiency and waste, not only in terms of dollars, of which we have a relative abundance, but in terms of that Einstein dimension, time, of which we have too little.

There are some facts we have to face. One is that cities can be too big, too impersonal, too unresponsive to changing conditions and attitudes. The result is a swallowing of the individual, subordinating him to the city and making him dissatisfied or discouraged in his ability to meet changing conditions and in his efforts to provide a better life for himself and his family. By the same token, cities and towns, particularly rural towns, can be too small, lacking in variety of life-styles and in opportunity for social and economic advancement. Chances for educational advancement can be lacking as well as social and cultural diversity and stimulation. The consequence in the too small town as in the too big city can be the same—dissatisfaction and discouragement.

One alternative is the creation of entirely new towns and cities, totally planned, totally designed to attack the problems which will confront us before we reach the turn of the century. What can the creation of these new communities accomplish? Two primary goals: First, they can help to provide a better life for residents of existing metropolitan regions where growth will take place by putting land to more efficient use. Second, creation of these new communities can provide a stimulus for decentralization. They can deliberately encourage the creation of entirely new urban centers and the expansion of smaller ones as alternatives to the expansion of our existing metropolitan regions.

We have a program within the Department of Housing and Urban Development which has as its purpose the creation of these new cities and towns. It is the New Communities Act, a program of federal guarantees to private developers and grants to public bodies. The purpose of these guarantees is to tap new sources of money for new community development.

With income tax forms ever present, it is of interest to know that this is one program that does not have a multibillion-dollar price tag. Only in the case of default would federal funds be required in substantial amounts. Fees and charges for these guarantees will make this program as self-sustaining as possible.

While the creation of entirely new cities and towns may be a new experience for the United States, at least in modern times, they certainly are not for much of the rest of the world. There are new communities either under development or in the late stages of planning in at least 50 countries. They occur in every continent and in every kind of country from the highly developed to the less developed.

The quantitative role these new communities will play in housing and in providing jobs and places to shop for the 100 million new citizens we will have by the turn of the century has yet to be determined. But these new cities and towns have the potential for qualitative importance as well.

Perhaps the best way of explaining what new communities might be is to explain what they should not, what they must not, become. They should not develop into a sort of super country club with a built-in federal guarantee, isolated and insulated from the reality of what is happening in our cities and to the rest of our country.

Escape was not the reason for the creation of the New Communities Act. Instead, that act and that program can be an aid in solving the problems of our central cities, suburbs, and rural communities by offering meaningful alternatives and by taking some of the pressure of additional population off our already overcrowded urban areas.

It will be necessary to continue our aid to other communities within our economy, particularly aid to our hard-pressed central cities. They are sitting on that stove that Einstein mentioned, and they cannot wait for us to build alternatives.

These new communities can provide an environment for better living for all kinds of people—of all income levels and all races and religions—at a minimum cost to you, the taxpayer, and a maximum return toward solving our pressing problems. It can—indeed it must, the law requires it—provide housing of various types and prices for a variety of income groups, including units both for rent and for sale. These new communities give us a chance to test new materials, new techniques, and new designs in planning for the future, and in social innovations in cultural, educational, and recreational facilities. They give us an opportunity to attack pollution on a basis of partnership between all levels of government, industry, and business, not by attacking the problem after it becomes a crisis, but before.

One of the most exciting proposed uses for new communities, and one of the most difficult to achieve, will be to build them in areas which in the past were largely rural and isolated from commerce and industry. These new rural communities can be built either in areas away from population centers or wrapped around existing small towns. They can depend upon the older community for basic services and structures such as schools, local government, and utilities until the difficult first years of development are over and the new community begins to build its own economic base.

Perhaps more than any other member of our society, the farmer understands the necessity of planning ahead and of basing his plans for the future upon hard-headed realism tempered with hope and a prayer. Finally, at long last, we are beginning to look at our national problems in much the same way. We have begun to realize that we are not separate communities of central cities, of suburbs, and of rural communities. We are one community with slightly different facets, independent to be sure, but interdependent as well.

The long-range goals of this administration are, not to hold the line against our problems, but to get out ahead of them. We intend to plan and build for generations, not simply to make-do with makeshift programs inadequately thought through and too often devised on the spur of the moment.

Albert Einstein was a pioneer. His discoveries shaped generations yet to come, as will decisions made on a domestic growth policy. They will determine the shape of communities and the quality of life they will provide for generations yet unborn. Einstein realized there is one thing you cannot do in this universe, and that is to stand still. We either go forward, or our problems swallow us and we go backward. There is no doubt in any of our minds as to which way we want to go.

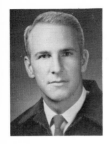

GREGORY BAMFORD

Past President
Future Farmers of America

13 | FARMING HAS A FUTURE

There are two basic resources to be considered in the seventies. You know them, we work with them all the time, but we never really identify them as such. These two resources are the land and her people. From these come the only true accumulation of wealth, knowledge, and progress that we can obtain.

The land is responsible for an accumulation as we plant a seed and it is nurtured—with the help of the elements—by man. At the end of a growing season it has produced many times more than the single seed that was planted. The beautiful thing about this is that it can occur again next year. Another seed can be planted in that same soil, on that same land, and it too will produce manyfold in its growing season. This second production of the seed does not cancel out or destroy the possibility of future production of the seed in that same soil if it is taken care of properly. This is true accumulation.

People operate in a different sense in that they are manufacturers of ideas, viewpoints, and opinions. One does not necessarily have to cancel out a previous idea to produce a new one. The second can complement or improve the first. We are trying to work with the land and the people in producing a good agriculture and a good future for this country.

I am concerned about the way the younger generation looks at the future of agriculture, the future of America. I would like to discuss some of the things that are going on in the minds of young people like myself as we look to the seventies.

We are excited about what is going to happen in the seventies. We are not pessimistic, but solidly optimistic. Whatever progress comes or whatever events occur, progress is not going to be automatic. Success will not occur without planning and foresight during the seventies.

We know our farm population is declining and have good reason to believe it will continue to do so in the years ahead. We see headlines like this: Youth Leaves The Farm For City Job. Here is a typical article:

In the glare and glitter of other professions and the fever for rapid money making, farming has apparently lost some of its old-time respectability. The stream of young people flows from the country to the city, and the boy who braves the current and intends to be a farmer is a rare boy indeed.

That article could be in just about any publication you might pick up today, but it actually appeared in the 1892 edition of the Board of Agriculture report for Indiana. You can see that the concept of people moving from rural to urban America is not totally new. In those days if a boy could not make it in the city, he could come back and still make a go of it with Dad on the home farm. Today that is not true. If a boy can make it in production agriculture, he can certainly make it in other jobs.

I am reminded of a story told by Howard K. Smith related to him and other reporters by President Lyndon B. Johnson about an old man named Ezra who was hard of hearing. He was finally persuaded by some of his friends to see a physician. After an examination the doctor found that Ezra also had a severe drinking problem. The doctor recommended that Ezra quit drinking to see if his hearing improved. About two weeks later the doctor happened to pass Ezra on the street and spoke to him. Ezra obviously didn't hear the doctor and walked right on by. The doctor wheeled around and grabbed him by the arm and said, "Ezra did you follow my recommendation and stop drinking, and did your hearing improve?" It took several repeats before the doctor could get through, but Ezra replied, "Yes, I stopped drinking and my hearing definitely improved, but I decided that what I was drinking was so much better than what I was hearing that I just went back to drinking." There are a lot of us in society today that might like to solve our problem that way but it does not always work.

The USDA has put together some facts and projections for 1980. Between now and then, there will be no major war—but no real peace, either—no major depression, a rising per capita income of 50 percent above the 1964 level, a healthy economy with a gross national product expanding to $1.125 trillion, inflation of 1.5 percent to 1.75 percent per year, a U.S. population by 1980 of 235,000,000, and an increase in the rate of generation and application of new technology for agriculture.

With these presumptions the USDA projects increases in per capita consumption of beef, chicken, turkey, vegetable fat, fruit, vegetables, and cereals other than wheat. They project decreasing per capita consumption of pork, eggs, fluid milk, cream, butter, animal fats, potatoes, wheat, cotton, wool, tobacco, and fats and oils.

Total consumption will rise because of the expanded population. Farm prices will rise, but so will costs. No one can readily predict which will win the race. Productivity is expected to rise about 2 percent per year due to increases in yields and efficiency. Farm output is projected to expand 50 percent over the 1957 level, with the livestock and livestock products output rising a little less than this, and crop output to increase a little more.

Exports will have to rise, but our higher costs and protectionism in critical markets will make it more difficult to ship products abroad. Farm programs similar to those we have now will still be with us to help revitalize rural areas, as the trend toward fewer farms and farmers continues. Farms will become larger, whether defined by acres, by sales of products, or by levels of investment.

One of the prominent things I see in the seventies is the increase in importance of the agriculturally related professions. They must broaden, they must strengthen themselves in order to serve production agriculture. In the minds of all people connected with agriculture, the goal must be to improve production agriculture for America. Marketing, processing, distributing, educating, informing, and all other related services that we now talk about as agribusiness are extremely important.

New agribusiness technologies or professionals must be developed to meet the needs in agriculture today. I am referring to such things as young people becoming established in production agriculture and such things as estate planning and tax counseling. I have been very outspoken in the last year or so about the need for someone to help farmers with these kinds of problems. The banker does not really have the ability to instruct farmers or evaluate their worth in these respects. Attorneys cannot advertise and solicit farmers' business in tax counseling, nor can accountants. There is really no one defined in our society and agriculture today that can sit down with a farm family and help them decide how their operation should continue to the best advantage of all involved.

This multibillion dollar business in America has a very loose organization for management of capital and resources—but here is the real kicker for me—and for the transfer of these resources to future generations.

One of the problems that young people face today in going into production agriculture is obtaining even the start their parents had in making an efficient and meaningful unit. A lot of these problems could be alleviated if fathers and mothers, families in general, would sit down and plan a course of action for the future years and generations. Many estates are eaten by inheritance taxes and by inefficiency in division. This is causing a lot of problems for young people as they look to production agriculture.

The capital requirements for agriculture are astounding as you look to the future. Mammoth amounts of capital will be needed for young people or anyone engaged in production agriculture to continue to increase efficiency and to operate economic units. The magnitude of investment that a young person or a farmer must face is overwhelming. They need all the help that they can get, and they need the ability to evaluate and decide their courses of operation.

My professors at Colorado State University tell me there are three ways that young people can get involved in production agriculture, farming, and ranching in this country today—marry it, inherit it, or work it. It is becoming more and more impossible to work it under the prevailing concepts that many young people hold.

Young people who want to go into production agriculture are going to have to look at it somewhat differently during the seventies than it has been viewed in the previous 15 or 20 years. It is as inappropriate for a young man to move directly into production agriculture on the scale it is going to have to be in the next ten years as it is for a young person to step from the ranks of college or high school and expect to walk into a small manufacturing concern of $300,000 to $400,000—or upwards into millions of dollars as we look to the future.

It is very important that young people have patience as they move into production agriculture. They should not rule themselves out of the agricultural world if they cannot immediately go back to the farms and ranches. Those that do go back are going to demand tremendous contributions from other areas. We have to have people who can provide the information, who can relate to us the developments that are occurring, and who can provide the other services of inputs and marketing outputs of market-oriented agriculture that we do not have today.

There are several ways to draw together these challenges and opportunities for young people in the seventies. The first of these is education. The time is past when we can survive and improve by trial and error or when we can totally rely on past experience. We need constant education to keep aware and abreast of new developments in agriculture. Specialization demands that farmers tap and use other people's knowledge. We cannot be masters of all trades. Many people will be needed to produce this information. Who can do the job in this agricultural chain? As young production agriculturalists we are going to have to draw from all resources and decide what we can use and what will be beneficial for us and for the people around us.

Computers are terrific. They are doing in a matter of seconds computations that formerly took days, weeks, and months. But there is still no substitute for common sense. People will still be needed to analyze and apply the information that they have at their fingertips.

There is a delicate balance between textbook knowledge and the common sense approach to production agriculture that is going to have to be met. It will require participation by farmers in developing what they need rather than resistance to new ideas as they are presented. Farmers are going to have to become involved, to solicit the things they want, and to plan accordingly.

It is very important that the young people going back to the rural areas of America do so with open minds, with the idea that they can improve their communities, that there are things to do in agriculture, and they must act quickly.

We hear a lot about moving urban America to rural America. New concepts and a rotation of philosophy will be needed for us to accept this and to achieve what the concept is capable of doing for our rural communities and for the people who are moving there.

Technology, methods, machines, seeds, and fertilizers are constantly becoming outdated. Education is essential to promote an attitude of acceptance toward new ideas. Honesty, integrity, character, and thrift do not become outdated. We need the solid, stable people with whom agriculture and farming have been identified for years. But at the same time, we must be progressively adventurous, attempting new things, searching for new horizons, and being aware of the world around us. Farmers as they look to the seventies and beyond, are going to have the same benefits as other businessmen. They are going to have better transportation systems and better communication. They are going to know what is going on in the world, and they are going to be a part of it.